Audacity to Love

About the author

Dr Anne Merriman, MBE, MB, BCh, DCH, DTM&H, MCommH (Lpool), FRCM (Nig), AM(Sing), FRCP (Edin), FRCP(Ire), FJMU, DSc(Hon) is Founder and Director of Policy and International Programmes, Hospice Africa and Honorary Teaching Fellow, International Observatory on End of Life Care in the Institute for Health Research, Lancaster University, UK. Born in Liverpool in 1935, Anne has spent 28 years working in Africa (including 10 in Nigeria as missionary doctor and 17 in Uganda), 7 in SE Asia, 8 in the UK and 5 in Ireland. She introduced palliative care into Singapore in 1985, which became an accepted form of care with the founding of the Hospice Care Association in 1989, while Senior Teaching Fellow in the Department of Community, Occupational and Family Medicine (COFM) in the National University of Singapore. Today this service is one of the best in SE Asia.

Anne returned to Africa in 1990, initially to Nairobi, before founding Hospice Africa, introducing palliative care to Uganda in 1993. Presently she heads Hospice Africa's International Programmes, supporting new initiatives in Nigeria, Cameroon, Sierra Leone, Malawi, Ethiopia, Zambia, Sudan and Rwanda, more recently seeking a model for Francophone countries for a model to suit their different health service and needs. Her concern is the relief of the suffering and provision of holistic care to the millions of patients and families in Africa suffering from or affected by cancer and/or AIDS. Anne is Founder member and the Founding Vice Chair of the Board of both the Palliative Care Association of Uganda (formed in 1999), and African Palliative Care Association (formed in 2003). She is also Board Member of Hospice Africa UK and Hospice Africa Uganda. She is a past Board Member of the International Association for Hospice and Palliative Care (IAHPC) and is presently Vice President for E Africa of the African Organisations for Research and Training in Cancer (AORTIC). Her contribution to health and relief of pain in the world has been recognised with many awards including an MBE for services to health in Uganda and an individual award for contribution to the spread of palliative care in the world by the International Association of Hospice and Palliative Care (IAHPC).

Audacity to Love

Anne Merriman

The Story of Hospice Africa

bringing hope and peace for the dying

THE IRISH
HOSPICE
FOUNDATION

First edition published in 2010 by Irish Hospice Foundation
Morrison Chambers (4th floor), 32 Nassau Street, Dublin 2
http://www.hospice-foundation.ie

Hilary Elfick's poem 'Hospice Uganda', first published in H. Elfick and D. Head,
Attending to the Fact – Staying with Dying, Jessica Kingsley Publishers, 2004, is
reproduced by kind permission of Hilary Elfick and Jessica Kingsley Publishers.

The article 'Living while Dying' by Dr Anne Merriman, first published in *Contact*,
no. 122, October 1991, Christian Medical Commission, Geneva, is reproduced by
kind permission of the Christian Medical Commission.

Illustrations from Sheila Cassidy, *Sharing the Darkness: The Spirituality of Caring*,
Darton, Longman & Todd, 1988, pp. 179–80, are reproduced by kind permission of
Sheila Cassidy and Darton, Longman & Todd.

Edited and designed by:
Martin Noble, Martin Noble Editorial, Iffley, Oxford, UK
http://www.copyedit.co.uk

ISBN: 978-0-9534880-9-4

Printed and bound in Ireland by:
Spectrum Print Logistics, Unit 4044,
Citywest Business Campus, Naas Road, Dublin 24

Contents

Dedication   vii
Why 'Audacity to Love'?   x
Preface   *by Jan Stjernsward, Chief of Cancer and Palliative Care*
          in WHO Geneva, 1980–96   xi
Acknowledgements   xiii
List of figures, colour plates and tables   xiv

PART I   SETTING THE SCENE   17

Hospice Uganda, *poem by Hilary Elfick*   19

1   Introduction   21
2   'To Help the Suffering of Africa'   24
3   From Medical Missionary to Palliative Care Consultant   28

**PART II   HOSPICE AFRICA:
              STORY AND DEVELOPMENT   33**

4   What Is Palliative Care?   34
5   A Short History of Palliative Care   42
6   The Birth of the Light   46
7   Hospice Africa in Utero   51
8   Hospice Africa Uganda: Birth Pangs   66
9   Initial Support   72
10   Challenges and Blessings of Colleagues and Governments   84
11   The Birth of Mobile Hospice Mbarara and Little Hospice
     Hoima, 1998   93
12   HAU and Palliative Care in Uganda Today   113
13   A Day in the Life of a Hospice Nurse in Kampala
     by Rose Kiwanuka and Martha Rabwoni   116

PART III   HOSPICE AFRICA:
PRINCIPLES AND PRACTICE   **125**

14   Spirituality   127
15   Development of the Hospice Ethos   145
16   Moving and Shaking in Hospice Africa and Beyond   154
17   Me, Myself . . .   169
18   New Initiatives, Donor Experience in Africa   178
19   Brain Drain, Costing and Clinical Standards   182
20   Hospice Africa Worldwide and the Struggle for Funding   188
21   The Man with the Key Has Gone   209
22   The Story of Affordable Opioids in Africa   223
23   The Unforeseen   256
24   Passing the Baton   263
25   Dying in Uganda   268
26   So What About My Own Death?   272

Appendix A: Living While Dying (first published in *Contact*,
               no. 122, October 1991, Christian Medical
               Commission, Geneva)   275
Appendix B: Do's and Don'ts for Volunteers
               and Health Workers   276
Appendix C: Ethos and Spirit of Hospices in Africa   278
Index   285

Dedication

Dame Cicely Saunders

This book is dedicated to the memory of Dame Cicely Saunders, who inspired the world to care for the dying, and took away the terrible dread of dying in pain for many. But freedom from pain, now recognised worldwide as a human right, is still denied to many in Africa.

It is also dedicated to my African family in my home in Kampala, where I am looked after and tolerated so well, to the team which started with three in 1993 and is now 135 in three hospices in Uganda, and to the community volunteers who reach those who have never seen a health worker, giving hospice access to the suffering in their homes while giving their care and time freely.

To Lesley Phipps and her family in Liverpool, UK, who have been with us every step of the way since I first explained the vision in 1992. They are part of the team in Uganda and, with the assistance of other friends, extend their caring to all Africa. This vision has been taken up by many on the Board of HAU in Uganda.

To all those we have helped or who have helped us in so many countries in Africa, each one of you is important to our patients and families and you have contributed with your dedication to this story.

Finally, this is dedicated to the patients and families we meet daily. You are the inspiration for the work. Your patience and care for each other, your care within your communities, are still well entrenched in your culture. I pray that you never lose your audacity to care for each other.

Anne with international students, November 2009.

All proceeds from the sales of this book
will go directly to Hospice Africa
to help continue and expand the work.

*

*'In palliative care
we are on the coalface of death.'*

*

*'Every pain that is relieved
and every symptom that is improved
is a little resurrection for our patient.'*

Why 'Audacity to Love'?

I HAVE CHOSEN the title for this book because I believe that the audacity to love is the quality most needed by all those working in hospices, giving palliative care to patients.

Audacity indicates that we are brave and willing to stand up for love, the love of our patients and families and for each other in the teams.

Love is the basis of all that we do. Loving each other we are willing to confide, to share, to accept constructive criticism so that we can be moulded to be the person who is there for the patient. Then we will be able to defend the ethos with each other and those who do not understand.

The palliative care mission comes from the love for the patient and family, loving them as we would ourselves or our family members.

Audacity to Love implies that we do not have other agendas in our work.

I realise that this is looking for perfection and that none of us is perfect. However we can still aim for the stars.

Our organisation, Hospice Africa, was originally inaugurated with this aim. We must be strong in our love and ready to defend patient care.

In writing this book, I have tried to emphasise the idea that we are all human but even those of you who have a special calling to care for the suffering and the poor need to approach the task with a heart of love, knowledge of the modern methods of managing pain, knowledge of the symptoms and awareness of everything that is involved in holistic care. Each of us needs to be willing to sacrifice ourselves at times, and to care with integrity for the sake of the patient and each other.

All we need is the ***audacity to love***.

Preface

Professor Jan Stjernsward, MD, PhD, FRCP(Edin)
Chief of Cancer and Palliative Care in WHO Geneva, 1980–96

*Dr Stjernsward shows the world the emblem of pain control in Africa, the
frangipani flower, whose milk, painted on Herpes Zoster, controls the pain.*

Audacity to Love is a book of hope and achievement, written by the
Founder of Hospice Africa for volunteers, donors and students of
palliative care, for those who may wish to help in Hospice Africa
Uganda (HAU), and for anyone who knows in their hearts that we can *all*
make a difference.

Palliative care and hospices for patients with advanced malignant
disease such as cancer have developed rapidly since the late 1950s when
Cicely Saunders, founder of the modern hospice movement, came to East
London. In 1967 she started St Christopher's Hospice and a year later
inaugurated modern home care for the dying. In the 1970s hospices
developed in the US, Canada, Australia, South America and Zimbabwe.
However, it is in Africa that there has been the greatest need for
palliative care since the rise of the AIDS epidemic. In most African
countries AIDS is on the increase but in some it is starting to reduce.
Cancer, however, is on the increase and already today kills more people
in the world than AIDS, TB and malaria combined. By 2020 in Africa
there will be one million deaths a year from cancer, representing 10% of
the world's cancer deaths.

Hospice Africa was conceived as a support group for an African
hospice which would be a model not only for the country in which it was
based, but for all African countries so that hospice philosophy and care

could be adapted to the cultural and economic requirements of each country. Anne Merriman tells the story of Hospice Africa for the first time, tracing its spiritual and religious associations with the Catholic Church, the importance of figures such as Fabiola in the early centuries after Christ, and her own role in the 1980s while teaching in Singapore. The story of this miracle of care began in Singapore in 1984 with the first survey of patients who were sent home 'because there was nothing more to be done'.

In Nairobi, Anne realised the huge need in Africa for palliative care after witnessing the suffering in Nairobi in 1990. After working for Nairobi Hospice as Medical Director and in the UK, Anne and her colleague undertook a feasibility study in four African countries, seeking a suitable country for a model. After Anne moved to Uganda it became the first country in Africa that made palliative care part of its National Health Policies and Strategies (1999–2000) and the first country in Africa to introduce free oral morphine for use in the home when prescribed by a registered prescriber. (Kampala became the location for the newly founded African Palliative Care Association some years later.)

I have worked intermittently but intensively with Anne for twenty years. Her medical background as a specialist in geriatric medicine, with a degree in International Community Health and practical hands-on working experience not only in Liverpool, but especially in Nigeria, Singapore, Kenya and Uganda on the one hand and her strong Christian belief on the other, are the key factors for all Anne has achieved through her strong personality. Anne is adventurous, determined, stubborn like a mule, direct, honest, humorous, observant, receptive, tolerant and has charisma and innate ability to get things done. Thousands of flowers bloom wherever she has walked in life. She is one of those lucky ones who can say they have had a positive impact for the betterment of mankind.

Anne tells the personal stories of those she worked with as well as of patients, of lessons learned in countries such as Nigeria, and of support received in setting up HAU. Finally she explores the hospice ethos – with the hospice as host and the patient as guest – and the spiritual aspects and principles behind palliative care, the problems and challenges the hospice movement faces and, ultimately, the importance of the special calling of working with the dying.

Jan Stjernsward
Borringekloster, Svedala, Sweden,
15 May 2010

Acknowledgements

S O MANY PATIENTS and friends, both professional and non-professional, have brought this book to reality. However a few must be singled out.

First the patients who have embraced the concept of hospice and made it work in Africa today. Secondly the many friends who have stayed in my home in Kampala, visited patients and seen the impact of the work here, and who have suggested we write down the story of the miracle of Hospice Africa.

I would especially like to thank Clare Muvaney, Noel Gavin, Emily Quinn, Abby Probasco, Hannah Merriman and others, including many patients, all of whom gave us permission to use their pictures to promote the work of Hospice Africa.

Autumn Fielding, volunteer extraordinaire, came in 2008 after a chance meeting at the internet section of a hotel in Clifden, Ireland. Wondering what an old lady was doing on the internet, she learned about our work and offered to come out a few months later. She spent six months with us and, among other areas, took on the book typing as I dictated it to her. She offered advice and suggested areas to add in to the story. This meant that I was talking to someone rather than writing a narrative and this helped so much!

Betty Babirye, my PA, has supported me for many years in her times with HAU but most particularly through the period of writing this book. In spite of huge tragedy in her life she always remains cheerful and manages to uplift me!

Eugene Murray and the Irish Hospice Foundation have supported the telling of the story every step of the way, both with advice and financial support.

Other assistance has come from Dr Ita Harnett and a host of Irish volunteers who have come and witnessed a miracle that has changed their lives and the lives of those they have helped. Nick and Di Rose, friends for many years and recent volunteers, gave outstanding support and suggestions. These many friends encouraged the writing of this book for the hospice teams of the future.

Lynn Alexander, my dear friend for 25 years, witness to the struggles and achievements in Singapore, has supported the telling of this story from the start. She is now a volunteer for the book with our editor, Martin Noble. Although separated by the Irish Sea, these two have worked diligently, guiding me and learning from each other.

Donors are mentioned only for the early days, as so many have joined us since. However the donations in time and skills from the pensioners in the charity shops in Old Swan and Ainsdale, Merseyside need a special mention. But to all donors, large and small, for your understanding and willingness to share our mission, you have my deep gratitude.

Finally, I gratefully acknowledge all others who have played a part, big or small, in this story. With their help, Hospice Africa has brought peace to many, and inspiration to all, and has made a difference in Uganda and Africa.

Anne Merriman
Kampala, Uganda
15 May 2010

List of figures, plates and tables

Figures

Dame Cicely Saunders   vii
Frontispiece: Anne with international students, November 2009.   viii
Dr Jan Stjernsward with pain-controlling franjipani flower   xi

1.1	The light of hope: sunrise over Lake Victoria, Kampala.	21
1.2	The light is the smile brought to the suffering child.	22
2.1	Anne just after the Biafran war, 1970, with a malnourished child, at Sacred Heart Hospital in Obudu, SE Nigeria.	24
2.2	Mum and Dad on bicycle, 1952; Bernard 1947.	26
3.1	Ward round in St Joseph's Hospice wing, 1985.	30
4.1	A holistic approach to palliative care.	36
4.2	Treatment realities for HIV/AIDS: Western countries, 1993.	37
4.3	Treatment realities for HIV/AIDS: African countries: 1993.	38
4.4	Treatment realities for HIV/AIDS: Uganda, 2008.	38
4.5	Treatment realities for cancer: Western countries, 1993/2010.	39
4.6	Treatment realities for cancer: African countries, 1993/2010.	40
4.7	The continuum of palliative care (WHO, 1986).	40
4.8	The continuum of palliative care in Africa (WHO, 1986).	41
4.9	Disease modifying therapy, supportive care and palliative care.	42
5.1	Cicely Saunders, nursing in her early years.	44
6.1	Sister Geraldine, pioneer of palliative care, 1989.	47
6.2	Nurse Brigid Sirengo, 1991, with a patient at Nairobi Hospice.	48
7.1	Nurse Fazal Mbaraka, 2003, returning to Uganda to celebrate ten years.	53
7.2	Akpan (1993) at St. Luke's Hospital, Anua, Uyo, Nigeria.	62
7.3	Akpan's diseased breast revealed.	62
8.1	Nsambya VMM House, 1993, our first home.	68
8.2	Margaret with a younger me!	70
9.1	Receiving the keys of our first HAU home, now Merriman House, Makindye, 1994.	74
9.2	Rose Kiwanuka assists a patient to get home in the first land rover, 1993.	74
9.3	Board of Advisors (1995) with Martha Rabwoni and Micheal McGoldrick.	75
9.4	Our first volunteer nurse, Brigid Kakande, with Bashir, 1993.	77
9.5	First team with land rover, in Ndebba, 1994.	81
9.6	Early picture of child with Burkitt's lymphoma.	82
9.7	Betty, our first secretary, helps Robert, daycare, Ndebba, 1994.	82
10.1	A child waits for the team to finish with her mother.	88
10.2	The Blue Book in English and French.	92
10.3	Medical students from Makerere on mobile rounds.	92
11.1	MHM Team (1999); Brian and Clare Fitzgibbon with Karen.	95
11.2	Wilson Tumwine, now Lord Mayor of Mbarara.	97
11.3	The youngest walker at the Tenth Anniversary walk.	100

11.4	Home visit patient during the early days at MHM.	102
11.5	Dr Stella on *borda borda* on home visit.	105
11.6	Team at Nile Special beer warehouse, Hoima.	105
11.7	Nurse Martin, LHH, at the patient's home.	111
11.8	MHM Team, May 2010.	112
11.9	Palliative care bag carried by nurses and doctors on home visits.	112
12.1	Hospice Africa clinical team, Makindye, Kampala, May 2010.	115
13.1	Mary McAleese, opening of Mary McAleese lecture theatre, 2001.	117
13.2	Specialist Palliative Care Nurse Charlotte examines a patient. *Photo courtesy of The Lancet.*	119
14.1	Dr Liz Namukwaya and PC Nurse Octivia with Sarah, 2007.	138
15.1	The patient and family are the centre of our care. Octivia Naziwa with patient and family, 2007.	147
15.2	Anne with a patient (Noel) at home, 2008.	153
16.1	Dr Lydia visiting hospice at a PCAU update, 2008.	156
16.2	Children in Cancer Institute. James able to smile. *Photo courtesy of Abby Probasco.*	157
16.3	Dr Mhoira and her palliative care team in Mulago Hospital, 2009.	158
16.4	Dr Robert Twycross, heir to Dame Cicely.	160
17.1	Autumn Fielding, volunteer, the catalyst for this book in 2008.	171
17.2	Mother Mary Martin (1892–1983), founded MMM in 1937.	172
17.3	Hannah Merriman volunteering in 2010 with Rayan.	175
18.1	Little Hospice Hoima (LHH) staff	180
18.2	Catherine Nawangi washes a patient's wounds at home.	181
18.3	Catherine Ruwambaya, volunteer coordinator at HAU for ten years.	181
19.1	Palliative care Nurse Jerith on a home visit in LHH.	183
20.1	Marge celebrates 90th birthday at charity shop, Liverpool, with Ann and Pete Purcell.	192
20.2	Jim Bennett in the French charity shop.	194
20.3	Anne Lloyd-Williams with Dr Lydia at meeting in Cape Town.	196
20.4	Rose, my first nurse and the country Director of PCAU. *Photo courtesy of Abby Probasco.*	197
20.5	Micheal McGoldrick with his daughter.	201
20.6	The Centre of Excellence in 1993.	202
20.7	New Clinical Centre of Excellence, funded from Ireland, 2010.	202
20.8	Mr and Mrs Scheer. Day 1 of married life.	205
20.9	Archbishop Paul leads 10th Anniversary walk for MHM.	206
20.10	Dr Judy Hills who started Hospice Africa USA in 2006.	207
21.1	Singapore conference in Palliative Care 1988: Dr Cassidy (UK), Dr Goh (Singapore) and Dr Takeda (Japan).	218
21.2	The doctor and priest, protected by their roles (Sheila Cassidy, *Sharing the Darkness*: Figures 6.1 and 6.2, p. 179).	220
21.3	Patient meets doctor and priest as human to human (Cassidy, *Sharing the Darkness*: Figures 6.3 and 6.4, p. 180).	221
22.1	Peter Mikajo makes up oral morphine in the pharmacy at hospice.	223
22.2	Map of countries in Africa with affordable oral morphine for use in the home, May 2010.	225
22.3	Level of palliative care development in Africa, 2006.	228
22.4	Lucy Finch on a home visit in 2004.	231

22.5   Orphans being cared for by the Sisters in Zambia.   233
22.6   Frehiwot, aged 17, in Liverpool. My Ethiopian daughter.   236
22.7   Sister Tsigereda with Catherine on a home visit in Addis, 2009.   238
22.8   Mrs Sola Fatumnbi of Lagos. Pioneer in Nigeria.   239
22.9   Prof. Olaiten Soyannwo, heart of the hospice at UCH Ibadan.   239
22.10   Catherine and team in provincial hospital, Bamenda, 2008.   246
22.11   Esther Walker and Dr James Russell with patient, Freetown, 2007. 248
22.12   Dr Nala Gaffer at Radiation and Isotope Centre, Khartoum (RICK). 252
22.13   The light is coming to Rwanda.   255
24.1   A patient, now trained in reflexology, helps another patient.   264
24.2   Dr Siobhan Kennelly from Ireland with CVWs, December 2004.   265
24.3   UCD Fellowships for Dr Lynch and Anne for work in Uganda, 2007. 265
24.4   Dr Jack Jagwe advocating in Nigeria.   266
25.1   Remembering Daddy: memorial service at Hospice Uganda, 2009.   270
25.2   Coffin retail boomed during the AIDS epidemic.   273

Colour plates

1.   Fabiola.   161
2.   The total pain of a child. *Photo courtesy of Clare Muvaney.*   162
3.   Frangipani tree, our emblem of pain control in Africa.   163
4.   Pawpaw seeds dried and crushed – ideal, affordable laxatives.   163
5.   'James' 2007 with his baby and tumour, 2009, having had
          traditional medicine applied to the tumour.
          2010, with the same child, after visiting hospice.   164
6.   Martha Rabwoni (MHM) consoling a patient dying in his
          own home.   164
7.   Dr Jacinto Amandua, Commissioner for Health.
          Photo courtesy of Abby Probasco.   165
8.   Mary McAleese signing visitors book, 2001, Makindye.   165
9.   Class of 2009, international students, on roof in Munyonyo.   165
10.   Sick children singing at Palliative Care Week, 2009.   166
11.   Dr Ludovik Zirimenya with patient on a home visit.
          Photo courtesy of Abby Probasco.   166
12.   Two broody volunteers, Tomas and Stu, with my grandchildren.   166
13.   With Cherie Blair receiving fellowship award, 2001.   166
14.   Community volunteers for hospice in Makindye, 2010.   167
15.   The youngest volunteer.   167
16.   Lesley and David Phipps with their two daughters.   167
17.   With Jim Bennett, prime mover behind HA France, 2010.   167
18.   Children enjoying activities at day care in HAU Makindye, 2010.   168
19.   My family in Munyonyo, Kampala.   168

Tables

12.1   Patient numbers, April 2010.   113
12.2   Breakdown of individuals trained by HA, 1993 to April 2010.   114
14.1   Core values of Ubuntu.   132
22.1   Estimates from population, prevalence of cancer and
          prevalence of AIDS patients in need of palliative
          care based on prevalence of HIV.   227

PART I

SETTING THE SCENE

Hospice Uganda
by Hilary Elfick

[*In this poem, Hilary captures the sadness that encompassed Uganda in 1997–98
due to the AIDS epidemic and the ever present cancer.*]

Hoima, 24.10.97

They say that Adam first drew breath in Africa

and certain I have seen his garden hung with mango, coffee, maize,
and watched the stalks of millet bow and curl before the wind.
And through the shades of vast savannah
I have seen the herds and flocks that once he named –
the elephant and vervet, and the shy low squirrel and the porcupine.

I never saw the serpent

but I did see the path where he has wormed
and left his spittle on the puffy cheek of dying child
and scoured away a young girl's fertile time. And here's
a man who hoes his field until he slims[1] with falling sickness
quiet into his furrow, and here's a granddad that has lain neglected
these wet months upon a foetid sheet. And there's a maid
whose belly swells with child who will not last his first full year,
and here's a youth whose every knot and tuft of hair
have dropped to show the snake's imprinted skin.

---

[1] 'slim' = AIDS.

19

Go forth and multiply? The sap still surges when the sun has fallen.
We say that man acquires his own deficiency;
we call our kind a syndrome.

And we, who make such careless jibes
from our thin quarantine, what can we bring
into these meadows washed with heavy rain,
along these red roads, scarred and pitted
with the blood that runs in Africa?
What pills, what powders, what fine potions can we root
to cover up the dribble of his passing?

Through touch of mist I see this nation's colours stretch
across the sky in bow that pales and leeches into dusk.
In these green blades close by the path I see
the sullen clots that slump and catch the evening light
against a prison hut where this old warder's wife is hunching in her flux,
tongue stiffened in its yellow coat, where hard beams of an equatorial noon
scorched eyes that fleck and flinch and cannot cry.

What parody of Eden's this dark hut
where child, whose mouth swells too grotesque to close,
lies trembling in a pulse that pounds two hundred beats a minute?
What God can we now walk beside at twilight
unless we first have washed him in his fraying blanket caked with waste,
as once again we watch him twist and wait to die?

But this was where first breathed a man.
That is what, at last, will burst the heart.
And still the pineapples are ripening in the fields.

Hilary Elfick, in H. Elfick and D. Head,
Attending to the Fact – Staying with Dying,
Jessica Kingsley Publishers, 2004

1   Introduction

Figure 1.1 *The light of hope: sunrise over Lake Victoria, Munyonyo, Kampala.*

THIS BOOK is being written for all those who may come to work with palliative care in Hospice Africa Uganda (HAU) and throughout Africa, for volunteers, donors, students of palliative care and colleagues who come to see the miracle of care that started long ago amidst the suffering witnessed in Nairobi in 1990.

My aims, in writing this book, have been to provide a survey and history of palliative care in Africa; to chart the growth and development of Hospice Africa and Hospice Africa Uganda from a personal point of view; to tell you about working with the sick and terminally ill as I have experienced it; to explore the ethos and the spiritual and ethical principles behind hospice and palliative care; to offer practical advice for those intending to work in the area of hospice and palliative care; and, in writing about all this, to preserve the philosophy of dedicated volunteerism, encouraging those with more to give to those with less. I also hope I can talk with honesty about myself and my own journey, even if it means occasionally putting myself in a bad light.

The story of Hospice Africa began in Singapore in 1984 with the first survey of patients who were sent home 'because there was nothing more to be done'. It is only now, on looking back, that I can see that I was being led, as were those who came with me and who had the same vision:

> Lead kindly light, amidst the encircling gloom:
> Lead thou me on.
>
> Newman, *The Hound of Heaven*

Nor did I realise, when I introduced palliative care into Singapore in 1985, that this light was to lead me back to Africa where the suffering was so much greater. When I was a doctor in Nigeria in the 1960s, I too had sent patients home from the hospital, telling them 'There is nothing more we can do.' Yet we never saw what went on at home after that. In Nairobi I was to see this for the first time and to realise the huge need in Africa for palliative care. It is essential that the story of where we came from and how we arrived here today (2010) be told, so that we realise that miracles can happen when the carers care and when our patients become our guests.

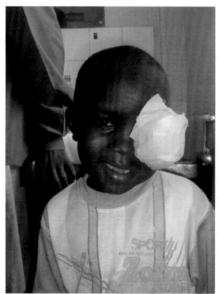

Figure 1.2 *The light is the smile brought to the suffering child.*

In spite of this miracle, we sometimes fail our patients and families because of our own human weakness. We must be aware of this, and we need to be able to work with our own failings and those of others. We are called to a special vocation, whether we are at the coal face seeing patients, or in the support sections bolstering those at the coal face. Every one of us is special and needed. So in telling you the story and talking about our ethos, which is so essential if this work is to continue throughout Africa, please keep in mind as the story unfolds that this is our history to date and *you* are the future.

While following the light, I have come across individuals, some of them carrying all the force of their organisations or place in life with them, who have tried to blind me to the light or extinguish it altogether. These have been very painful times for me as a person and often for the others who have surrounded me and supported me. Yet, looking back, I can see that these very persons, unknown to themselves, were instruments in helping us to turn a corner where the light shone more brightly. So I am grateful to them for their share in God's plan. During these episodes, I have been unable to see the way forward and it is only in looking back that we can see that even in the darkness, a greater Light has had hospice in His hands.

2 'To Help the Suffering of Africa'

This is my brother. I know those shoes.[2]

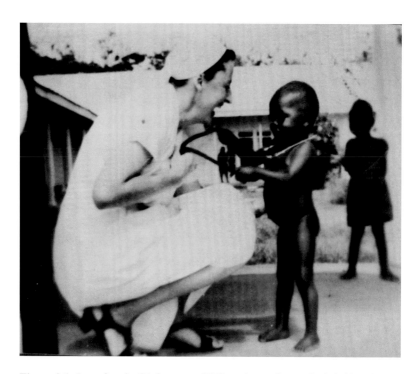

Figure 2.1 *Just after the Biafran war, 1970, with a malnourished child in the malnutrition unit, Sacred Heart Hospital, Obudu, SE Nigeria.*

I WAS BORN in Liverpool seventy-five years ago. My parents were also born in Liverpool but my four grandparents were born in Ireland. Thus I was brought up a true Scouser (Liverpudlian) for the first eighteen years. I went to Ireland at the age of eighteen and then lived with the Irish for the next twenty years as a Medical Missionary of Mary (MMM). This was following my call, recorded and told by my mother,

---

[2] Desmond Tutu, *No Future Without Forgiveness*, Doubleday 1994, p. 192, quoting from a brother of a murdered man in South Africa.

that I had stated at the age of four: 'I want to go and help the suffering of Africa when I grow up.'

After twenty years as a religious Sister and Missionary, including ten as a doctor in Nigeria and Ireland, I returned to secular life, working in Merseyside to be with my mother who had had a heart attack and was failing. After her death in 1981, I completed a Master's degree in International Community Health at Liverpool School of Tropical Medicine, which included a spell of research in India. I then went to teach at Universiti Sains Malaysia (USM) in Penang, Malaysia, and a year later to the National University of Singapore where I stayed for six years, with the seventh year working with the fledgling Hospice Care Association, before returning to Africa in 1990.

It was in Singapore that we commenced a volunteer service of myself and nurses to carry out home care after work and at weekends. This eventually became the Hospice Care Association of Singapore which is now one of the finest services in the world, thanks to the strong dedication of Dr Cynthia Goh, Dr Rosalie Shaw, Sister Geraldine Tan, Canossian Sister, and the nurses who carried it forward. It was from here that Hospice Africa eventually came to be.

The twenty years as Medical Missionary of Mary had moulded me for my future in palliative care, although at the time I did not realise this. This is similar to many things that have happened in my life, both good and bad. There has been a divine guidance that I have only realised on reflection, looking back at my life. But along with many other gifts, these twenty years gave me the spirit of hospitality to all, a hallmark of the hospice movement.

My family was strongly Catholic. My mother was deeply spiritual; my father was a teacher – and a teacher with a degree, most unusual in those days. In spite of his degree he was dedicated to teaching the young and became headmaster of the very primary school we were attending. I had still three years to go before reaching the age of eleven and moving on to the grammar school. My father was also very musical and had taken plainchant as a subject at university, and from time to time played the organ at our church. He died at the age of fifty-four during my first year in Ireland as an MMM.

I was the third of four children. There were just seven years between us all, and only eighteen months between myself and my

younger brother, Bernard with whom I was very close. He died after a
very short illness at the age of eleven from cancer of the brain. This was
a huge shock to the family but my mother never forgot Bernard and
grieved for him until her death at the age of seventy-nine. I was very
influenced by this. Bernard had wanted to be a priest and in those days
boys went to the junior seminary at the age of eleven. Later my elder
brother Joseph joined the Salesians after National Service and was
ordained a priest in 1962.

Figure 2.2 *Mum and Dad fooling around on a bicycle, 1952; inset: Bernard
1947 who died 1948.*

I too wanted to be a priest and my first great disillusionment in my
young life was finding out that women were not allowed to become
priests! I could not understand such discrimination and I still feel the
same.

At the age of thirteen, I watched a film in the local cinema about very modern medical nuns in Ireland who were working in Africa. These were the Medical Missionaries of Mary (MMMs) founded in 1937. These Sisters could show a little hair at the front, the veil allowed the neck to be seen – and the ears! They wore their clothes eight inches off the ground (thus showing their ankles) and were allowed to ride bicycles. This was revolutionary!

I told my God, my mother and a nun at school that I was going to join them and indeed joined this very order at the age of eighteen in January 1954.

3   From Medical Missionary to Palliative Care Consultant

If we have listening ears,
God speaks to us in our own language,
whatever that language may be.
Ghandi[3]

AFTER ALMOST three years' missionary training and three years in the medical laboratory (one year single-handed), I joined the medical school at University College Dublin. Graduating in 1963, followed by one year's internship, I arrived in Nigeria in September 1964 for my first real taste of Africa. I was stationed at St Luke's Hospital, Anua in SE State. This was then a large teaching hospital. It was also the place where the MMMs were first founded, and which had inspired me in the film I had watched at the age of thirteen.

Mother Mary Martin, the founder, had made her first profession from this foundation but in a hospital bed in Port Harcourt. St Luke's Hospital was very advanced in 1964. It had departments of medicine, surgery, paediatrics, ophthalmology and dentistry. Each was headed by a person of consultant status, and newly graduated doctors from University College Hospital (UCH) Ibadan were accepted for recognised internship following inspection from the university.

These were turbulent years for Nigeria as the Biafran War broke out in 1967. This was the year I left Nigeria because of illness. As well as studying for my higher degree in internal medicine, I returned to Nigeria three times during the following ten years. The first was in January 1970 as the war came to a halt, and I was again stationed in Anua. The second was after the war and in Obudu, an area of Nigeria on the border of the Federal and Biafran areas which had been taken by either side and the hospital robbed on several occasions.

That was a special year, working with generous girls, who had left school at standard 6 (11+ age in UK) and trained as nurse aids. We were occupied by the Federal (victorious troops) who thought they could have access to our medical services and our nurses as the whim took them.

---

[3] R. Attenborough, *Words of Ghandi*, Wildwood House, London, 1982, p. 74.

My third tour in Nigeria was back in the specialist hospital at Anua, where I was the consultant physician but also the counterpart to the obstetrician on night duty, carrying out the obstetric emergencies.

In 1973, I left Nigeria and the MMMs to return to England. I had thought for two years about my calling. I felt that although I was very happy with the MMMs, I could manage to move further with my work without the regulations that were inhibiting me. At the same time I learned that my mother was ill, and having recovered from a myocardial infarction was finding it difficult to manage alone. So I returned to Liverpool.

During the next eight years, I worked in Geriatric Medicine in Liverpool, Manchester and then back to Merseyside as consultant to an area service which had been initiated a few years earlier but failed after the resignation of the initial consultant. Together with the new Geriatric team covering a large area of St Helen's and Knowsley, we managed to get the service back on track and it is still working today.

In this service we were looking after acute hospital beds and beds in long-stay wards where many people were having prolonged dying under difficult circumstances. This is when the need for palliative care was brought into focus. The elderly needed pain and symptom control and a sympathetic consultant and team to bring them to peace. I started practising palliative medicine and teaching not only the geriatric team, but surgical and medical teams in both hospitals.

It was there that I realised the great need for the palliative care approach initiated by Dame Cicely Saunders and I invited her to come to Liverpool to talk to our teams. At that time there was no palliative care service in the Mersey region and in fact the first establishment for a palliative care consultant did not occur until 1993. However when Dame Cicely came to talk at Whiston Hospital in 1981, we were turning the audiences away as we could not fit them all in! It was a most popular day and the first two Macmillan nurses commenced with a scholarship fund through Dame Cicely for the area of St Helen's and Knowsley.

*

My mother died in 1981 and I began to move on to my calling to work abroad. The Master's course in International Health included three months in a developing country. My country was India and I was attached to Benares Hindu University with three classmates, two from Africa and one from the West Indies. My friends were completely culture shocked and stayed in Benares, but I travelled to Calcutta then to Kerala and as far as Cape Comerin, on my own, interviewing the elderly of India. This was an intense three months and we studied the Government, the health system and the religions. I came away feeling that I had had a deep experience of a new culture.

On the recommendation of the Dean at the School of Tropical Medicine, I applied for posts in Community Medicine departments in USM, Malaysia and National University of Singapore. USM was fastest at accepting me and I left for Malaysia in 1983. After one year, I transferred to Singapore. This was because, following an invitation to an interview, I learned that Singapore was facing a problem with an increasing elderly population. This was due to recommending two children per family for twenty-five years, with financial restrictions from the third child on. Their population pyramid was almost standing on its head! Thus my experience in geriatric medicine would be most useful there.

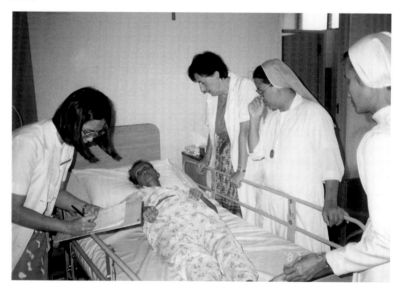

Figure 3.1 *Ward round in St Joseph's Hospice wing, 1985; from left: Dr Cynthia Goh; patient; me, Sister Lucia Chan and Sister Geraldine Tan.*

My time in Singapore allowed me to research into the needs of the elderly and also the dying. Finding that many with cancer were sent home to die, I started with a small group of volunteer nurses to follow the patient in their homes. Singapore is an island 11 miles by 22 miles and in 1984 it had a population of 2.5 million, so it was easy to visit the homes. However, it had to be done after work and weekends as my department was not clinical and did not allow this as part of our work.

After three years we had looked after 450 patients and gained enough experience to commence training health professionals, doctors, nurses and pharmacists, although it was important for us to have an affordable analgesic for severe pain that could be taken by mouth. The pharmacists came up with a formula for pure morphine and this formula later became the gateway to holistic palliative care in Africa.

PART II

HOSPICE AFRICA: HISTORY AND DEVELOPMENT

4   What Is Palliative Care?

Definitions of palliative care

THE WORLD HEALTH ORGANISATION (WHO) defined palliative care first in 1990 and later in 2002.

The 2002 definition states: 'Palliative care is an approach that improves the quality of life of patients and their families facing the problems associated with life-threatening illness, through the prevention and relief of suffering by means of early identification and impeccable assessment and treatment of pain and other problems, physical, psychosocial and spiritual.'

But definitions can be confusing. Often donors will change definitions to suit their need for numbers. So it now needs to be stated categorically that pain control alone without support care is simply anaesthesia. Support care without pain and symptom control is just that – support care. This care is very valuable and has been available in Uganda and other parts of Africa before palliative care was introduced to Uganda in 1993. Kitovu Home Care, TASO (The AIDS Support Organisation), Nsambya Hospital Home Care and other AIDS support organisations were in place in Uganda. These organisations were founded by some very inspirational people who met the challenge of sickness and death of the AIDS epidemic head on. This was comparable to the support care available in Western countries before Dame Cicely Saunders carried out her research into pain and symptom control and started the modern hospice movement in London in 1967. In fact, support care is all that is needed in the HIV trajectory until the 'client' becomes a 'patient' due to critical illness or at the end of life.

Palliative medicine is a holistic approach that must include pain and symptom control as well as care for the psychosocial, cultural and spiritual aspects of the patients and families. In fact, often pain and symptoms block the holistic approach. A patient and family will devote all their attention to the pain and suffering, not allowing themselves time or energy to focus on other aspects. It is not until the pain is relieved that these other issues can be addressed.

Hospice care and palliative care

So what is the difference between hospice care and palliative care? Many people today still think hospice is a building where you put people that are dying. This is not true. 'Hospice' is now recognised as a philosophy of holistic care which can be given to the patient in the place most appropriate for themselves and their families. This place is being recognised more and more as in their homes, and this is particularly true in Africa.

The word hospice comes from Latin word *hospitium* or the Greek word *hospes*. These words mean hospitality and the word denotes the relationship between the guest and the host. And for us in palliative care it is between the patient and the carer. The patient is our guest and this means that they will have choices in all decision making until the end of their life. Sadly, this is not the case in hospitals today. Thus it is very important that the word hospice does not disappear for it symbolises and embodies this important approach to care.

So how does the term 'palliative care' come about? The word palliative comes from the Latin word *pall* which means blanket or covering. It denotes the comfort that is given through palliative care.

The word 'palliative' was first coined by Dr Balfour Mount of Montreal, recognised as the founder of palliative care in Canada. In the early 1970s when he was introducing palliative care to Canada he felt that the word 'hospice' would not be respected in the Canadian communities because it was associated with a 'death house'.

I found a similar situation when I was teaching in Singapore. Sago Lane was a row of 'Chinese death houses' in which patients were on a conveyer belt to the graveyard, passing through the undertaker en route.

Holistic care demands that the carer must have empathy. In Figure 4.1 you will see that I must look at my patient as if he or she were me and as if this were my death. How have my life experiences helped me to help others? One must also look at questions such as: What is my relationship with God and spiritual experience? Do I feel comfortable talking about spiritual issues to my patient? Have I a relationship with my own team so that I can support others and feel supported myself?

All this is necessary to the carer who is to provide holistic care. So we must take time to reflect so that we can be all in all to our patients, whoever they may be.

Figure 4.1 *A holistic approach to palliative care, seeing suffering as part of our own lives.*

Africa and palliative care

Palliative care (PC) has come into Africa on the back of the AIDS epidemic. In most countries in Africa, AIDS is on the increase but in some countries it is starting to reduce. Cancer is now estimated to have killed more people in the world than AIDS, TB and malaria combined, and by the year 2020 in Africa there will be one million deaths a year from cancer which represents 10% of the world's cancer deaths.

So if we look at what is available for patients with AIDS and/or cancer in Africa today and compare it with what is available in Western countries, it is really very shocking. This can be seen from Figure 4.2, which represents the treatment realities for HIV/AIDs in Western countries in 1993, and Figure 4.3, which represents the treatment realities for HIV/AIDs in 1993 in African countries. Since antiretrovirals (ARVs) became available in the 1980s, if you were born in the West and your CD4 count[4] indicated that you were in need, you would receive ARVs immediately which would often be fronted by the insurance companies or government.

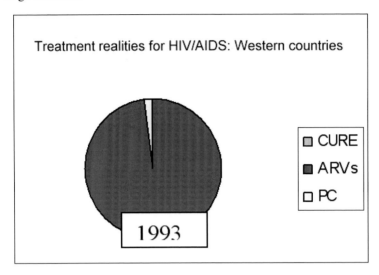

Figure 4.2 *There is no cure: treatment realities for HIV/AIDS in Western countries, 1993. Plentiful ARVs mean relatively little PC is required.*

---

[4] HIV attacks a type of immune system cell called the T-helper cell. This cell carries on its surface a protein called CD4, which HIV uses to attach itself to the cell before gaining entry.

The T-helper cell plays an important part in the immune system by helping to co-ordinate all the other cells to fight illnesses. A major reduction in the number of T-helper cells can have a serious effect on the immune system. HIV causes many T-helper cells to be damaged or destroyed; as a result, there are fewer cells available to help the immune system.

A CD4 test measures the number of T-helper cells (in a cubic millimetre of blood). Someone uninfected with HIV normally has between 500 and 1200 cells/mm^3. In a person infected with HIV the CD4 count declines over a number of years. Treatment is generally recommended when the CD4 test shows fewer than 350 cells/ mm^3. However, guidelines vary slightly between countries and these are constantly debated. When the CD4 count reaches the recommended level to start treatment, other factors may also be taken into account, such as viral load and opportunistic infections. (Information obtained from: http://www.avert.org/antiretroviral.htm)

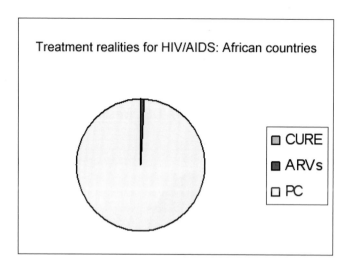

Figure 4.3 *Treatment realities for HIV/AIDS: African countries: 1993.*
Few ARVs mean a relatively large amount of PC is required.

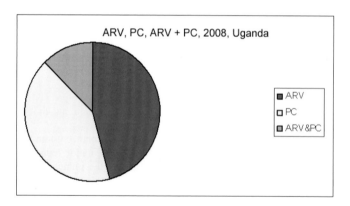

Figure 4.4 *Treatment realities for HIV/AIDS: Uganda, 2008.*

Today in Africa, ARVs are becoming much more available and are often given freely, thanks to donors such as the President's Emergency Plan for AIDS Relief (PEPFAR) and the Global Fund (see Figure 4.4). However, in Uganda only 60% of the people who require ARVs actually receive them. People in the villages continue to die without ARV intervention. This is due to many factors which will be discussed later but the economy and faith in traditional healers are common reasons for late presentations for cancer and AIDS. However it can be seen that the presentation for HIV/AIDS is changing and the numbers requiring care for critical illness or end of life care are reducing. For those assured of continuous ARV's, AIDS is no longer a life-threatening illness and many will die of another condition.

Figure 4.5 represents the picture regarding cancer and treatments available in Western countries. This indicates that in the West approximately a third will receive curative treatment such as radiotherapy and chemotherapy, a third will be cured and a third will receive palliative care.

Figure 4.6 shows the reality regarding cancer and treatments available in African countries. About a third of African countries have no radiotherapy or chemotherapy available. Apart from South Africa and previously Zimbabwe, countries that do have radiotherapy or chemotherapy have only one centre available for the entire country. It is estimated that while only 5% of the population will reach such a centre, less than 5% of those who reach the centre will actually benefit from it. Often, many people either come too late or cannot afford to pay for it. Thus, people in Africa with cancer suffer long-term pain and often die in severe pain and without support.

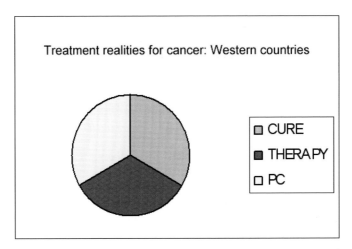

Figure 4.5 *Treatment realities for cancer: Western countries, based on estimated average annual figures for 1993–2010.*

Anne Merriman

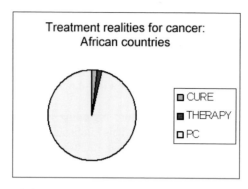

Figure 4.6 *Treatment realities for cancer: African countries, based on estimated average annual figures for 1993– 2010.*

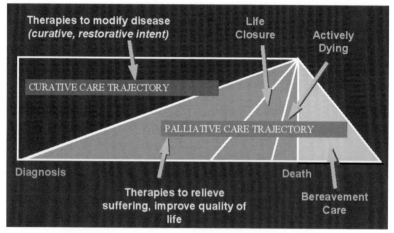

Figure 4.7 *The continuum of palliative care (WHO, 1986).*

In Figure 4.7, the continuum of palliative care is shown in diagrammatic form. This was written with cancer in mind. The line from diagnosis reaching death which cuts palliative care from curative care needs to be raised, for Africa, as you can see in Figure 4.8.

In Africa, curative treatment is available to so few that palliative care is needed for almost all patients and is usually the only option for them, if it is available. However as the pattern of illness has changed in HIV/AIDS, palliative care would not be suitable for the care from diagnosis. These are now 'clients' for the support care services, who will need support care for their psychosocial, spiritual, cultural and other needs including stigma at different times during their disease trajectory.

Now that we have looked at the main definitions of palliative care and why it has become so necessary in Africa, it is time to step back and consider its history and background.

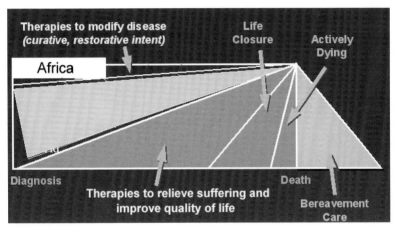

Figure 4.8   *The continuum of palliative care in Africa (WHO, 1986).*

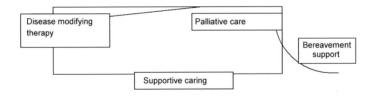

Figure 4.9 *The relationship between disease modifying therapy, supportive care and palliative care from R. Twycross,* Introducing Palliative Care, *4ᵗʰ edition, 2003. Adapted for Africa by author, remembering that only an estimated 5% are able to access oncology in Uganda.*

5 A Short History of Palliative Care

THE FIRST RECORD of a patient in need of palliative care is recorded in the Gospel of Mark 5:25–26.

> There was a woman who had suffered terribly from severe bleeding for twelve years, even though she had been treated by many doctors. She had spent all her money, but instead of getting better she got worse all the time.

This woman was similar to many patients coming into hospice today. They have spent all their money on treatment from health workers who neither talk to them nor tell them the truth. This woman reached a cure in her body and soul in her meeting with Christ and in experiencing his love and care.

The second recorded event in hospice history is about a holy woman in the early Church named Fabiola. Three hundred years after Christ, she opened her home to pilgrims who were travelling across Europe to the Holy Land. Some of these pilgrims were simply tired, but some were sick and even died in her hospice. Later, similar hospices were founded on the route to the Holy Land and were usually run by holy women. Eventually the places where people were taken when sick in England, before the Reformation, were called hospices. These were mainly run by the religious orders of the day. During the Reformation all religious houses were disbanded. The people no longer had anywhere to take the ill and begged the king for a place that would look after the sick. This is when hospitals were born. Sadly the relationship of hospitality between host and guest is not a priority in hospitals today. But the hospice and palliative care ethos has the power to change this.

Coincidentally I have a painting of Fabiola, which was brought to my home by a cousin, Father Bob Callan, ordained in Rome in the 1930s. He brought copies of two original paintings as gifts to my mother. One was of Fabiola and the other of 'Our Lady of the Wayside' (Maria della Strada). These two pictures hung above the piano in our sitting room. I did not know who the beautiful lady was until we looked at the back many years later. The picture was given to another cousin by my mother, and when the cousin died, was passed on to her friend, who graciously gave it back to me in 2006 when she knew of my interest. My life has been scattered with such gems of coincidences or light, slowly coming together like a kaleidoscope, revealing that there was a greater plan designed by a Great Being, leading me on.

In 1842 the term hospice was first used to describe a place for the terminally ill. In Lyon, France, Madame Jeanne Garnier founded five hospices. The present building is still in Lyon and is called Fovea Aged Home. The French concept of a hospice today is more that of a building in which the elderly may be looked after. However, they now have a strong palliative care association and this may change.

In 1834 in Ireland, Mother Mary Aikenhead founder of the Irish Sisters of Charity, commenced St Vincent's Hospital in Dublin. She died in 1858 at the convent in Harold's Cross. The following year Our Lady's Hospice for the care of the dying, opened in memory of Mary Aikenhead, at the Harold's Cross site. This is a very famous hospice today which practises modern palliative care. Recently, Harold's Cross has given two rooms to Hospice Africa Ireland, a centre for coordination and fundraising.

In 1900, five Sisters of the Irish Sisters of Charity came to East London and started home care for the dying. In 1902, St Joseph's Hospice obtained thirty beds for the dying poor. It was to this hospice, in 1957, that the founder of the modern hospice movement, Dame Cicely Saunders, came as a young physician to research pain and symptom control for the dying. During her ten years at St Joseph's she was searching for the right way to start a modern hospice. The life of Dame Cicely Saunders is written in great detail elsewhere.[5] She had been a nurse and a social worker before she commenced reading medicine.

Dame Cicely had trained as a nurse and almost immediately had to leave that profession because of 'back trouble'. She then became an almoner (social worker). During her time working with patients she met a Polish refugee, David Tasma, dying of cancer in 1948. She watched as the medical personnel spent time at the bed of every patient except his, avoiding his bed, for they could do nothing more for him and they did not have the skills to communicate with a dying person. She confided in her patient that one day she would have a home where people who were dying would be the centre of care. He in return left her £500 in his will for a window in her home. This window can be seen today to the right of the entrance at St Christopher's Hospice in London.

---

[5] Shirley du Boulay and Marianne Rankin (2007) *Cicely Saunders: The Founder of the Modern Hospice Movement*, London: SPCK.

Figure 5.1 *Cicely Saunders nursing in her early years.*

However, even more valuable were his words to her which now echo in every hospice to each of us from our own patient: 'I only want what is in your mind and in your heart.'[6]

Dame Cicely later worked in St Luke's Hospital with Dr Norman Barrett, a surgeon who was using morphine on a regular basis, anticipating cancer pain, so that the patient's fear of the pain returning was removed. She wanted to spread the word to other doctors of the great work he was doing. He explained that other doctors would not listen to

---

[6] Ibid., p. 35.

her unless she was a doctor, so Cicely went to medical school in her thirties. She did not go to become a doctor per se, but to gain a voice for the needs of the dying in the medical world.

After finishing medical school she commenced working at St Joseph's Hospice where she researched pain and symptom control for the dying. During this ten-year period, she consulted widely with both religious and secular groups while continuing to fundraise for her hospice. She even contemplated founding a religious order dedicated to care of the dying, but after much advice she decided against it and started with a dedicated medical team. In 1967 she opened St Christopher's Hospice and the modern hospice movement was born. Dame Cicely, who died in 2005, continues to be one of the most inspirational and influential people in the hospice movement.

In the 1970s the hospice movement was commenced in the US, Canada, Australia, South America and Zimbabwe, and in the 1980s in South East Asia and South Africa. During the 1990s it began to spread to Eastern Europe, India and to move more rapidly though other African countries. In 1987 the Royal College of Physicians in London declared palliative care a specialty in medicine, but it was not until 2007 that the USA also recognised it as a specialty.

6   The Birth of the Light

There are more things in Heaven and Earth,
Horatio, than are dreamt of in your philosophy.
Shakespeare, *Hamlet,* Act 1, Sc. V

I T IS ONLY in looking back that we realise that there is a presence in our lives guiding us. Usually the most painful times guide us into new directions and on looking back we are able to see that there was a reason for it all. The story of Hospice Africa started in Singapore.

From Singapore to Nairobi

In 1984, having been a clinician all my life, I found myself as Senior Teaching Fellow at the National University of Singapore in the Department of Community Occupational and Family Medicine. I had worked with the old and the dying in the British NHS before going to Singapore and my special interests were therefore the treatment of the elderly and palliative medicine.

Having completed a study on the needs of patients who were sent home to die from the hospitals, because there was nothing else that could be done for them, we found that they were dying at home in severe pain. We then had a conference to which we invited nurses, doctors and other interested people. This meeting looked at the felt needs of health professionals to fulfil the needs of the terminally ill. Sister Geraldine Tan, from St Joseph's Home for the Aged, Singapore, attended this meeting with Sister Mary Tan and others from the community of Canossian Sisters. Sister Geraldine, a nursing sister, had completed training in palliative care in the Royal Marsden Cancer Hospital in London.

The Canossian Sisters now came forward and offered to set aside twelve beds in their home, for hospice patients. It was recognised that many patients were dying and wished to do so, at home: thus there was a real need for home care as well. A volunteer group commenced, to provide a home care service. This comprised three nurses and myself. We worked with the pharmacists as they were preparing liquid morphine.

It was in Singapore that the formula for reconstituted oral morphine was first developed, which is now the only affordable and accessible Step 3 analgesic,[7] opening the gate to palliative care across Africa.

Figure 6.1 *Sister Geraldine Tan, pioneer of palliative care extraordinaire, Cannossian Sister, 1989.*

In 1989, the funding came to support a home care team and the Hospice Care Association of Singapore was born, supported by the Singapore Community Chest. Several other palliative care inpatient/residential and home care groups have since developed and the

---

[7] Step 3 analgesics are administered to patients at the most advanced stage of pain management according to the WHO analgesic stepladder: Step 1: non-opioid for mild pain; Step 2: opioid for mild to moderate pain; Step 3: opioid for moderate to severe pain.

work in Singapore was very much spearheaded by Dr Cynthia Goh, Sr Geraldine Tan and afterwards carried forward by Dr Rosalie Shaw. Rosalie published her book in 2009 about her experiences in home care in Singapore.[8] It brought back many precious memories to me of working with the families in Singapore twenty years ago at this special time of life. We all met in Singapore in September 2009 to celebrate with the teams, patients and families who have benefited. In return, many have given back to the service as volunteers. This is now one of the best services for cancer patients in the world, with 60% of all cancer patients passing through palliative care.

In the same year, 1989, I was invited to Nairobi with the possibility of becoming the first Medical Director of Nairobi Hospice, starting in 1990. Nairobi Hospice was the first hospice in Africa to be established with the needs of African patients in mind. Ruth Wooldridge, a nurse and wife of BBC correspondent Mike Wooldridge, witnessed patients coming home from hospital in severe pain. She knew that we had the knowledge to help such patients in the hospice movement and she began raising funds to form the Nairobi Hospice Charitable Trust, which was registered in UK.

Figure 6.2 *Nurse Brigid Sirengo with an early*   **Figure 6.3** *Dr Rosalie Shaw.*
patient at Nairobi Hospice, 1991.

In 1989 I found two nurses, Jane Moore from the UK and Brigid Sirengo, the first Kenyan nurse to be employed at Nairobi Hospice,

---

[8] Rosalie Shaw, *Soft Sift in an Hourglass: Stories of Hope and Resilience at the End of Life.* Armour Publishing, Singapore (2009).

working from a small hut without electricity and reading case sheets by candlelight. Going on home visits I met patients with advanced cancers, who were in severe pain. The strongest analgesic available was codeine, and this was available only to the rich. There were no Step 3 analgesics. I told the board of Nairobi Hospice that I would be unable to come unless there was affordable morphine for all patients in need. I left with them the formula for oral morphine and the address of where they could obtain morphine powder. Professor E. Kasili, Oncologist and Chairman of the Board, brought this to the government and for the first time affordable morphine came to Africa. The liquid morphine was made up in the pharmacy of Nairobi Hospital (a private hospital where the pharmacist member of the Board was working) and collected from there by the hospice team.

In 1990 I joined Nairobi Hospice as the first Medical Director. During my time there I recognised the terrible suffering that had been going on in Africa for years. In the 1960s while working in Nigeria as a hospital doctor, I was one of the many doctors who, when we could do no more, would ask the families to take the patients home. For the first time in Nairobi I was actually seeing what was happening to the patients who were sent home. And it broke my heart.

The work in Nairobi Hospice was so fulfilling as we saw patients in severe pain, having it relieved and reaching peace with their families and with their God before death. The team was wonderful and growing in the spirit of hospice. But it was here that I first experienced opposition to the spirit of hospice and palliative care from the bureaucracy inherited from the British and still alive and well in the African health systems.

Times became difficult for me at Nairobi Hospice. I was on a mission to spread the ethos of hospice and palliative care, which had been developed during my experience with hospice work in several countries. I was finding it impossible to develop this ethos at Nairobi Hospice due to the bureaucratic approach rising mainly from the Board. This was my first experience of the power of boards, which was a problem in Africa because palliative care was new and boards had as yet little knowledge of the ethos that the patient and family should always be the central reason for their decisions. Boards can, however, be highly supportive for new initiatives if carefully chosen, and brought in to see the hospice working in the home. This is indeed an area within Africa that needs research and reflective action for the future of the dedicated teams that work so well, but which, being fragile, can be broken.

After seeking advice, from God and locally, I decided that I would have to leave. However, early in 1991 Dame Cicely had invited me to write an article about the work we were doing at Nairobi Hospice. My article was based on a case study of a patient whose pain had been relieved and who was living very peacefully before death with the support of the hospice team. This article was published in October 1991, in the journal *Contact,* published by the World Council of Churches in Geneva, which was free of charge in many African countries. This particular edition was edited by Dame Cicely and my article is reproduced in this book as Appendix A.[9]

Around that time, as I have said, I made the decision to leave Nairobi Hospice. While struggling with reasons for leaving, I was asking God how he could introduce me to such a great need and then put me in a position where I would have to leave it. Letters started coming from other African countries where my article had been read, including Cameroon, Nigeria, Ghana, Senegal, Tanzania and Uganda. The letters asked me to bring to their countries what we had started in Nairobi. Their own countries, now devastated by cancer and more recently with the AIDS epidemic, were also in need. I realised that Africa was begging for a palliative care service suitable for any African country in resource-restricted circumstances. The idea of providing a model that was culturally suitable and affordable was born.

'God closed one door and opened another.'

---

[9] Anne Merriman, 'Living while Dying', *Contact,* no. 122 October 1991, Christian Medical Commission, Geneva.

7   Hospice Africa in Utero

Nothing could have prepared your heart to open like this
Once it began, you were no longer your own.
A new more courageous you, offering itself
In a new way to a presence you can sense
But you have not seen or known.[10]

IN 1993 WE DIDN'T have five-year plans and timelines, we just did things as they happened. Coming back to the United Kingdom, I needed a means of income so I tried to get a position in a hospice, preferably in the Liverpool area where I was setting up my initial support for Hospice Africa. But, believe it or not, Liverpool had no establishment in the health service for palliative medicine in 1992. So I took locum medical director posts initially in Myton Hamlet Hospice in Warwick and later in St Mary's Hospice in Birmingham. Both of these places were quite far from Liverpool but I would always return on the weekends, to meet with people who were supporting the new venture.

Travelling up and down the M6 was a way of life that year, but it was hard work and often sleep would overtake me due to fatigue from the work and the boredom of driving on a motorway! One day, while traversing Spaghetti Junction, a police car pulled me into the side. A big guy climbed out of the car and told me that he had followed me for some miles (I had not noticed him) and that I was zigzagging over the lane lines in an erratic way. He said he could tell I wasn't drunk – I was now wide awake with shock – but was I tired? I agreed that I was. He said he should give me a ticket, but instead was going to follow me to the next service station where I was to promise to go in and get a cup of coffee. True to his word he did, and I managed to get home safely … He probably saved my life.

The first two people that came seriously on board were Lesley and David Phipps. I had known Lesley since 1973, when we worked together in the first University Geriatric Medicine Team in the Northern Hospital in Liverpool. Perhaps it was the experience in that pioneering development with a wonderful leader, Professor Jimmy Williamson, that

---

[10] John O'Donohue, *Benedictus*, Transworld, 2007, p. 72.

gave Lesley and me the courage and vision to dedicate ourselves to the needy in Africa. David was a lecturer, in the Chemistry Department in John Moore's University. In 1992, these friends, in a rash moment, said 'We will help you in anything you are planning to do.' At that time they were the proud parents of twins, aged eleven.

The initial meetings of the future board were held in Liverpool. The constitution was ratified by a volunteer lawyer from Birmingham. The founding mission stated:

> The objects for which the Association is established are:
>> To *promote the relief of suffering* (so far as such purpose is charitable) *in all or any African countries* in such ways as the Association shall from time to time think fit, and in particular (but without prejudice to the generality of such object):
>
> a. By establishing, maintaining and conducting or supporting the establishing, maintaining or conducting of palliative home and residential care for patients with chronic or terminal illness in particular, but without limitation to the generality of the foregoing, for patients with incurable cancer, without regard to the race, creed or sex of the patient and by providing medical or other treatment and attention for such patients.
>
> b. By conducting or promoting or encouraging research into the care and treatment of patients and the families of such patients suffering from cancer or other terminal illnesses.
>
> c. By promoting or encouraging or assisting in the teaching or training of doctors, nurses, physiotherapists, students and other persons engaged in any branch of medicine, surgery, nursing or allied services, and in all methods of palliative care.
>
> d. By providing or assisting or encouraging the provision of spiritual help and guidance for any person providing or receiving such palliative care or any other person affected by the patients' terminal illness.

The objective of Hospice Africa was to be initiated by the forming of a 'model' in a country to be selected. This model would be affordable and culturally acceptable and capable of being adapted to other African situations.

It was decided to carry out a feasibility study in some of the countries that had requested a service. At that time it was difficult to reach these countries since there was no email and 'snail' mail was literally snail mail – it travelled very slowly. Now during the latter part of 1992, while locum Medical Director at St Mary's Hospice in Birmingham, I was joined by Fazal Mbaraka. She had worked with us as a palliative care nurse in Nairobi Hospice, and decided to help me set up the model hospice in Africa.

Figure 7.1 *My pioneer Nurse Fazal Mbaraka, who was closely involved with the birth of Hospice Uganda, returning to Uganda for our tenth anniversary celebration. Later we named one of our hospices in Makindye (Fazal House) after her.*

So now we had a real plan. But everything needed money. The funding for the feasibility study came from Ireland from the Civil Service Third World Fund. So we were able to carry out this study in the early months of 1993.

Fazal was born in Kenya of immigrants from Pakistan who came for the building of the East African railway. Her parents had built up a small farm in Eldoret which was the family home. Her mother had died when Fazal was young and she was brought up by her elder sisters. She had a younger brother and one older than her who was working at this time in a business in Eldoret. Her father was now elderly and the family were supporting him. Fazal had been brought up a Muslim but some time before she came to Nairobi Hospice, she had become a born-again Christian. She was so dedicated to learning through the Bible and attended church wherever we went, reading the Bible morning and night. Her father confided in me how impressed and proud he was of her dedication and spiritual outlook which enabled her to dedicate her life to the less fortunate. I was always welcome in her home and the home of her brother Mohammed and as we had to drive from Nairobi to Kampala several times it was a welcome break. Sadly her father had a stroke in 1992, but survived it and was managing in a wheelchair when we visited him on the feasibility study in 1993.

Fazal was a dedicated nurse who cared deeply for the suffering. She had gone to school in Eldoret, knew the people and the culture. She was a great asset to me over the year she was with me, teaching me many things as we came to decisions together on the way forward.

Fazal and I set out from England on the feasibility study in February 1993. We visited Kenya (Moi University), Nigeria (Lagos), Zimbabwe (Island Hospice, to learn from their experiences) and Uganda.

Kenya

We arrived in Kenya, and to my little house in Kileleshwa, Nairobi, which I was still renting. I had known I would be back in Africa but not sure where, so it was better to leave my belongings there. My two cats from Singapore were there and being looked after by my former 'live-in lady'. My car was there and moving ... so we were able to make contacts and to go to Moi University in Eldoret, who were very keen to have a palliative care unit attached to them. But I was alerted that another hospice in Kenya at that time might compromise Nairobi Hospice, as we would be competing for funding. Eldoret was Fazal's home and we would have liked to be there but we had to be unrestricted in this new venture with implications for the whole of Africa.

Uganda

So we crossed the border at Malaba and went into Uganda. There we met with Celia Stephenson and her friend, who was revisiting the places where she had worked for many years for the VMM (Volunteer Missionary Movement). She and her friend Anne were staying at the convent attached to Nsambya Mission Hospital. This hospital was one of the several mission hospitals that had sought answers to meeting the needs of the AIDS epidemic with the resultant rush of patients to hospital, by providing a home care service for such patients. Funding was coming into Uganda for the support of these patients not only with health provision but also with food, school fees and the support of widows and orphans. All of these services were being run from this wonderful hospital.

Nsambya Hospital was founded in 1903 by Mother Kevin who came out from Ireland and started a chain of services as well as the hospital. Their first service to the local people was under a tree. Gradually they got help to build a hospital which, in 1993, was the chosen hospital for most of the medical specialties and also as a training school for nurses. From the pictures of Mother Kevin and her helpers early on, Nsambya Hill was then fields. In 1993, it was the Catholic Hill of Kampala along with Rubaga Hill which has the cathedral. We found that Nsambya had its own cathedral then with many Catholic activities attached, including the Joint Medical Store (Catholic and Protestant Mission procurement of medications for the Mission hospitals), which we still use for the procurement of our morphine powder and other medications for palliative care.

Sister Rosemary Needham, FMM (Franciscan Missionary of Mary), was the accountant at the hospital, and welcomed us with open arms. 'You are coming for cancer patients? You are so welcome. All our activities are having to go to the AIDS patients and the cancer and other patients are being left out.' Apparently there was so much available if you were HIV positive that some patients, after being given the good news that they were negative, were going away crying because now they could not have school fees for their children!

Fazal and I were invited to stay in their convent. We were so relieved as we had nowhere to lay our heads and were living on a shoestring. So we worked out of Nsambya and travelled to other countries from there.

In Uganda we met with the Minister of Health, Dr James Makumbi. He was delighted to hear of palliative care and how it could assist the many who were dying at all ages. We did tell him we had come primarily for cancer. He was so supportive and agreed for the morphine powder to be imported. When we returned to Uganda from Zimbabwe and Nigeria the process moved forward.

Zimbabwe

Fazal and I could not believe we were still in Africa when we arrived in Harare. At that time the population was ten million. Wide tarmacked streets, dual carriageways, traffic lights and no potholes! The children were going to school in beautiful uniforms walking along the streets. The shops were full of amazing things not available in postwar Uganda. We noted in the report that this country was more akin to Scandinavia than Africa! A tropical, temperate climate made it an easy place to live in.

The team at Island Hospice made us very much at home. They had just been left in a will a beautiful little cottage across the road which was to be used for day care. It had two bedrooms, tastefully furnished with pretty flowered curtains and bedspreads to match. Did we feel at home! We slept there for the days in Harare, going out with the team and meeting different members of the team.

Island Hospice started up following the bereavement of the parent of a young woman in 1977. Home care commenced in 1980 and day care in 1992. The service used St Anne's Hospital for relief admissions and for terminal care of those unable to die in their own homes. The cost of admission was covered by private insurance or Government for the poorer patients of up to $400 per month. The cost of the Island Hospice patients was shared with the hospital and the hospice.

The hospice was serving all ethnic groups but the ratio of white to black in 1993 was 6:4. However this was moving rapidly towards more Africans benefiting as their needs were increasing with the HIV epidemic.

The white bereaved relatives took more time to work through bereavement than the African families because of the major bereavement problems in old age, similar to those in the UK. The average age of death was in the seventies, as compared with twenties to forties for the Africans. Also throughout the continents, most Africans have seen death from their childhood, and have to return to working hard to keep the rest of the family which in a strange way protects them from severe and protracted bereavement. We have so much to learn from Africa. This was reinforced in all the countries we were to work in later.

The team consisted of the Senior Administrator, Dave McElvaine, who was born in Zimbabwe, had a social work background and as such had a wonderful understanding of the local needs. He was supported by a part-time medical director, eight social workers and nine nurses, all able to drive, so therefore no drivers were employed. There were also five support staff including a cashier and part-time secretaries. The team were supported by many volunteers.

Each car had five safety devices against theft, and control of cars at the gate and in the hospice was extremely good. There was also a donated ambulance for their use with the air-rescue team. Once a week patients were collected from home and brought to the day care centre in this ambulance by the air rescue team. The two teams covered low-density areas (whites mainly) and high-density areas (mainly the African areas).

The team were well coordinated in seeing patients and each nurse had her own workload, which if it became too heavy was supported by another team. There was a lot of time for a bereavement coordinator who worked four days a week. They accepted bereavement referrals from not only their own patients but also from suicides, road accidents and coronary heart deaths. They had group counselling sessions. They also supported bereaved parents and grandparents. Education was mainly volunteer training at that time. Medical students had lectures and clinical placements with Island Hospice. Nurses came for three-day programmes. Local fundraising was well organised.

The computer operator doubled up for M&E (monitoring and evaluation). Morphine powder was available and an oral solution was made up and was available throughout the country from the Government store. Tablets of 10 mgs were also being made by a local firm, CAPS, in Harare. The local brand cost $40 for 100 tablets compared to the same tablet imported which cost $100 for 56 tablets. This was the best in Africa at the time. But life has changed in Zimbabwe since then and the economy has fallen.

This wonderful service has struggled to keep going through the troubles since 1993. But it is still a beacon for training and care in Harare. But this experience again helped us to realise that we need to be forever vigilant and know that what we plant can only be measured by what we do for today. We must be the best we can each day.

Nigeria

This was my first time back to Nigeria since I had left it in 1973. I had worked there for ten years with intervals in Ireland and as the first African country I had worked in I had a special leaning towards it as the site of the 'model'.

However Fazal and I were in for a culture shock. Two generations had been born and grown up into a culture of day-to-day survival since the Biafran war. Thieving was rife and Nigeria had earned a reputation as having one of the highest levels of corruption in the world. The airport was scary and coming outside even more so as we were grabbed by many hands wanting to exchange money, get us a taxi or anything else. The heat and humidity were familiar but no less a shock. I had always compared arriving into Lagos as going into a cinema with the smell of bodies and moisture. It had not changed in twenty years. I was (and still am) afraid of arriving in Lagos without someone to meet me.

We got into a taxi and asked to be driven to the Catholic Mission in Maryland. The taxi felt as if there were no springs and we thought that from time to time the driver just ran on his legs through a hole under the driver's seat! Riding downhill, the engine was turned off to preserve petrol and we cruised down to the bottom when the engine was put on again. We stopped precariously many times as we tried to move through the Lagos 'jam'. Slowly we moved as we were offered through the windows everything from a fridge to a fur coat for sale. A great way to shop from the car seat.

I vaguely remembered Lagos and knew that Maryland was close to the airport. After an hour and a half, I told the driver he was going the wrong way. We had passed signs for Maryland and kept going a few times. Eventually we arrived at the Mission and were met by a Nigerian Sister. The driver demanded $100. We started to bargain him down when the Sister took charge. She told him in pigeon English, in no uncertain terms, that he was letting down the whole of Nigeria by his behaviour. She gave him a real dressing down until, ashamed, he reduced the fare to $20.

I was looking for the Medical Missionaries of Mary, my own Sisters with whom I had worked as a missionary in the 1960s. I knew they were in Lagos, but now it was evening and we were far away so the Kiltegan Fathers, with whom I had also worked in the 1960s, took us in and gave us a home and that night brought us up to speed on Nigeria. The following day we went to the MMM house and later that day to Sr

Laurence Hoey, MMM, who was doing groundbreaking work in an area of Lagos called Amukoko, covering health services for 70,000 people within a 2 km area of the centre itself. She welcomed us and gave us hospitality and guidance during our time in Lagos.

We had planned for three weeks in Nigeria. This was mainly spent in Lagos, working with Mrs Fatumnbi, the founder of Hospice Nigeria, following the inspiration she received from meeting Dame Cicely and visiting St Christopher's in 1991. She had returned determined to help cancer patients dying in Lagos. Mrs Fatumnbi was a retired nurse of the traditional type whose husband was a surgeon. She had the contacts we needed to meet those who could make decisions affecting a new service. She welcomed us with open arms and got us the introductions to the Ministry of Health, the University Hospitals and the British High Commission. We also visited the University of Ibadan, where they were interested in setting up a palliative-care team. Much groundwork was laid down and we even formed a two-year plan with the Lagos team. The Ministry of Health agreed to the importation of morphine powder and were very keen to have the 'model' in Nigeria.

It being my first time back, I was anxious to visit the SE region where I had worked, trained and been introduced to Africa in the 1960s. I had a small illness while in Lagos, and during a day in bed took a picture of a candle by the bed looking exactly as I was feeling with the heat and humidity.

When I was better, I booked a bus to Uyo, a full day's drive away from Lagos. Leaving Fazal behind in Lagos with Sr Laurence, to carry on the local meetings, I left at 5 am for the bus park. The driver of the small minibus was named Patrick and I suggested he had been baptised by an Irish Kiltegan Father. Sure enough he had been born in the MMM hospital at Urua Akpan and given the name Patrick there! We immediately bonded and I was put in the front seat of the bus.

I had been warned not to carry my passport but a copy. At one point we were stopped and the police got me to come down. I was the only white on the bus. He asked for my passport and I gave him the copy. He asked me where the original was and I told him that I only carried a copy because the police might take the original. He laughed and let me back on the bus. It was true, the police were known to take the passports of visitors and hold them to get bribes.

Patrick took me for a meal in his home in Onitsha and we travelled on, arriving in Uyo in the dark. Uyo was the nearest town to St Luke's Hospital in the 1960s and was now a city with a university. The taxi park was full of small private hire taxis trying to get my fare to take me to the hospital. It was again very frightening. Then Patrick told them all to go, and put me back on the bus and drove me himself to the convent attached to the hospital where they were expecting me.

It was here that I learnt several lessons of God's work, why our plans and outcomes are so important in the five-year plans today for donors.

When I had arrived in Nigeria in 1964, this was the second most modern hospital in Nigeria. The first was UCH Ibadan. St Luke's had all the departments necessary for a teaching hospital, each department headed by an expatriate who was training the Nigerian doctors. The students from UCH Ibadan came to us for their internship. I had arrived straight after my own internship and had experience in every department, especially paediatrics, surgery and obstetrics and gynaecology. I was operating alone after the first few weeks – but that is another story for another book.

We had been training Christian doctors and nurses with a firm ethical background. There was a large school of nursing with most of the students being Ibo and Ibibio. The teams respected the senior staff and the sisters. We were encouraged in our work because we were producing some of the best trained and equipped nurses in the country. Our nurses were recognised as SRN in UK as well as their local qualification.

I could not believe the hospital now as I went around and found the structures in poor condition, patients lying on beds without sheets, nurses sitting around doing very little for the patients and having absolutely no respect for the Sister doctor who was taking me around, and had been there since 1959. It was now a government hospital with very little input from the Sisters. The present degradation was a result of the Biafran war and the ensuing lack of support from the Federal Government for the area declared as Biafra.

An expatriate doctor who I knew of, Dr Ann Ward, met us on the hospital tour. She had for years specialised in the repair of vesico vaginal fistula (VVF) and had set up a special clinic and operating area in Uyo with residential accommodation to allow these women to live there and build them up before surgery. Dr Ward's great work has relieved the suffering of so many women and enabled them to regain respect in their families and communities.

Dr Ward brought me a patient. Akpan will remain in my mind forever because although I could do little to help her, I was beginning to realise the terrible agony for my African colleagues when confronted with someone in severe pain that they could not relieve. Akpan had been admitted to the hospital with cancer of the breast. The mass in her right breast had been incised by a traditional healer and the tumour had eroded through the wound, producing the smell of dead tissue, so familiar to us who deal with cancer. In fact the smell is due to the putrefaction produced by anaerobic bacteria living in the dead tissue so that they produce a smell similar to that of a decomposing dead body.

We knew then and had known for many years that this could be controlled by using metronidazole; a medication found all over Africa as it is used for amoebic dysentery and other intestinal infections common in tropical climates. The tablet is crushed and applied to the area. It dries up the secretions and even stops bleeding if the wound is oozing, but most of all it attacks the anaerobic organisms and the resulting smell. Metronidazole was available in the hospital so now Akpan could join the rest of her family without the smell that had ostracised her.

But Akpan was in severe pain. Her cancer had developed secondaries locally, visible in the picture. She had not slept for some time. How helpless I felt! Here I was on a feasibility study, with no doctor's bag, no medications and the only analgesic in the hospital was paracetamol, a Step 1 analgesic.

I turned to God to ask, 'Why oh why have I been presented with Akpan when there is nothing I can do for her pain?' It was a desperate feeling of hopelessness. How many years would it take before affordable oral morphine would be available in Nigeria and how many years before it became available in SE State?

I meditated on why ... and suddenly I realised this was so that I could know what my African colleagues who cared would feel. Many left the profession and others became hardened to pain and just turned the other way. How sad for the caring professions in the whole of Africa! But now I could empathise with them as well as with my patients, and, thanks to the terrible burden of suffering of Akpan, this would hold me in good stead when dealing with frustrated trained health workers who were unable to get the medications required for their patients in many countries.

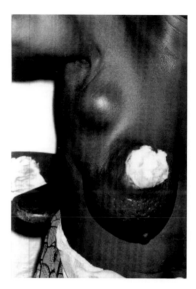

Figure 7.2 *Akpan, 1992, at St Luke's Hospital, Anua, Uyo Nigeria.*

Figure 7.3 *Akpan's diseased breast revealed.*

After my visit to St Luke's Hospital I travelled briefly to Port Harcourt to meet a great friend who was working in a village investigating the needs of the mother and child as part of her doctorate from the Liverpool School of Tropical Medicine. I then returned to Lagos and Fazal by bus.

The full report of this feasibility study is available in detail from Hospice Africa. However my memories are described above because of their effect on the experience we were about to face in setting up the model.

*

Uganda was chosen for the model for the following reasons:

1. It was just emerging from 25 years of war and full of hope.
2. People were very poor but they were in need of, and very accepting of, having a palliative care service, due to the burden of HIV and cancer.

3.　Uganda had the confidence of the international community for raising funds, whereas some of the other countries did not.
4.　The AIDS epidemic had increased the cancer level, and these patients were in terrible pain.
5.　The Minister of Health, Dr James Makumbi, accepted the importation of morphine powder which could be used to control pain in the homes of those in need in Uganda.

After completing the feasibility study in other African countries Fazal and I returned to Uganda. When we arrived in Uganda with very little money, the Franciscan Sisters at Nsambya Hospital offered us accommodation. These Sisters later offered us a small house in which we commenced the service in September 1993, but many events happened in the meantime.

In March 1993 we were invited to be guest speakers at the Combined Scientific Conference on the Management of Advanced Cancer, held in Lacor Hospital in Gulu. This hospital had the only chemotherapy and radiotherapy in Uganda at that time. This was a very enjoyable meeting for we met many key people who were to help us in the future.

The Honourable Minister for Gulu, Mrs Betty Bigombe, answered our address by asking us to start a branch of Hospice Africa Uganda (HAU) in Gulu and she promised to donate two acres of land. We actually made a note to do this when we were well established in Kampala but sadly, with the horrific fighting in Gulu, the radiotherapy and chemotherapy came to a halt. It was considered too dangerous for us to set up a hospice there. Mrs Betty Bigombe, a very brave lady with the courage of her convictions, continued for many years in this position and even met with the Lord's Resistance Army to release Gulu from the horrific fighting, and the terrible suffering arising from the stealing of the children, both boys and girls, from schools to become child soldiers and mistresses to the Leader and his soldiers.

*

Following the Lacor meeting, Fazal stayed in Uganda making local contacts while I returned to the UK from April to September 1993 to raise awareness and hopefully funding!

Meanwhile Hospice Africa was registered as a UK charity in Liverpool on 12 August 1993. The Mission was 'to support affordable and culturally acceptable palliative care for all in need in Africa'. This would be done by establishing a model in an African country, which could be adapted to the countries in Sub-Saharan Africa (see above, Chapter 7, p. 52).

The initial board consisted of Lesley and David Phipps, Celia Stephenson, Alice Davidson, Paul Hargreaves, and Pat Linnell. This group made up the initial Board of Trustees.

Background to Uganda, 1993

The British occupied Uganda from 1894 to 1962. The British passed over power to President Obote in 1962 but by 1970 it was a troubled country and in 1971 Idi Amin took over in a bloody coup. In 1973, Idi Amin expelled most of the Asians in Uganda, who had actually helped build up the economy of the country. Obote came back into power in 1983 but took over a country that had no discipline. Museveni led an army in the bush and overtook Obote in 1986. But the war continued in the north and is only now returning to normality. This was a war with the Lord's Resistance Army.

The twenty-five years of civil war up to 1986 had left the economy in ruins and the people in fear. Museveni was declared President and began to build up the country again. He was the first president in Africa to admit there was an AIDS problem in his country. Uganda had a population of 22 million, of which 52% of the population was below fifteen years of age and more than 55% of the population were not reaching health services. So we found elderly and young generations surviving, while the workforce, the middle-age groups, were disappearing.

The disease had been recognised and was locally called 'slim disease' for obvious reasons. Support organisations began to appear in Uganda in those years because the beds in the hospitals were completely taken up by patients with AIDS. Once the patients were discharged they needed support. Kitovu Hospital in Masaka was the first to provide home care for HIV patients, covering a huge catchment area. TASO, the AIDS support organisation, was commenced in 1989. This was an initiative by Noerine Kaleeba, whose husband Christopher, had died of cryptococcal meningitis, due to HIV. Her story is told in her moving book *We Miss*

You All.[11] TASO is now known all over the world for supporting people living with AIDS. The initiators of TASO were Ugandans who were infected or affected by HIV.

In 1993, Ugandan's cancer rate was on the increase. Kaposi's sarcoma, a marker for AIDS, was the commonest cancer seen at hospice and this continued up to the year 2002. There were no antiretrovirals (ARVs) or antibiotics, and antifungal agents were scarce and only affordable for the rich. Thus we were seeing people who were severely ill and often died within a few weeks after we first started seeing them. These people were young and from reviewing all of our annual reports, women made up the majority (60%). In Uganda, life expectancy was 38 years and HIV prevalence was considered to be 30%. People were poor and yet the people that we saw were well nourished, (except the slim disease patients who were unable to eat due to their illness). Most of the population was made up of subsistence farmers, without cash crops. Uganda, first called the pearl of Africa by Winston Churchill, will grow plants and food almost overnight. It is a very fertile country.

The first few years we saw a lot of very sad cases. Many parents were dying with unfinished business for their children. We saw tragic mothers dying shortly after childbirth and babies dying due to lack of safe breast milk. We didn't know it at the time but there was light coming at the end of the tunnel. But this didn't really take off until the twenty-first century. This is when ARVs became a reality and affordable to more in Uganda.

---

[11] Noerine Kaleeba and Sunanda Ray, *We Miss You All, Noerine Kaleeba: AIDS in the Family*, 2nd edition, SAfAIDS, 2002.

8   Hospice Africa Uganda: Birth Pangs

May memory bless and protect you
With the hard earned light of past travail;
To remind you that you have survived before
And though the darkness now is deep,
you will soon see approaching light.[12]

SEEKING FUNDS for the new venture, April to September 1993, I went to America, Canada, England, Scotland, Ireland and Singapore. The most successful country was Singapore. In the church I had formerly attended I spoke at all the Masses over one weekend and sufficient funding was raised to provide for a three-month service for a three-member team. This was from the Father Damien Society of Blessed Sacrament Parish in Singapore.

At that time the US and Canada had a policy of not providing funding for care of patients but only for prevention. Thus if I had needed condoms I could have accessed millions! Western governments are often not aware how much suffering a single policy, when brought down to village level, can bring to the patient and family.

However Ireland came up trumps, supporting me through the Agency for Personal Services Overseas (APSO) the government volunteer programme at the time. Other organisations like the Irish Teachers' Union and, in the following few years, the Irish Hospice Foundation, assisted us with small grants.

The Scottish Catholic International Aid Fund (SCIAF) funded our first training programmes for Health Professionals, and the Catholic Association for Overseas Development (CAFOD) in the UK supported the initial running costs and later the initial funding for Mobile Hospice Mbarara, in 1997–98.

While I was seeking funding, Fazal was in Uganda working with the initial supporters and looked after the first patient, Teddy, in June 1993. Teddy was a twenty-year-old girl with a brain tumour who died in early September 1993. Teddy's family have never forgotten the support

---

[12] John O'Donohue, *Benedictus*, op. cit., p. 130 … For Suffering.

Fazal gave to them and they have supported Hospice Africa Uganda (HAU) ever since.

Shortly after this Fazal had a terrible family tragedy: her father was murdered in his own home in Eldoret. Traditional Muslim burials must take place within twenty-four hours of death. Fazal got the news late due to the fact she had been moving around to different accommodations. She flew off in my elderly Nissan that I had brought from Nairobi, and drove from Kampala to Eldoret in record time. Just as she almost reached the location she crashed the car into a bridge. Luckily she was able to start it again and reached the funeral just in time, after which the car never moved again!

Although she was able to come back for just a week at a time over the next three months, she left the budding hospice on 31 March 1994, due to family commitments. As it happened, at that time we employed our first Ugandan nurse, Rose Kiwanuka, on 1 April 1994.

*

I returned to Uganda in September geared up to start the service, only to find that Fazal wasn't there: she was in Eldoret with her grieving family and had left the land rover, donated by the British High Commission, with a friend. I had never seen this car before and the last time I had driven a land rover was in the 1960s in Nigeria! Now I had to get in and go . . .

Fazal's friend met me at the airport, and with my luggage in the back we started to look for accommodation. By the end of the day we still hadn't found anything! Dead tired and constantly dozing off, I decided to go back to the Sisters and hope for their help again. Seeing how tired I was, they graciously took me in. Hence, it was in Nsambya Hospital that the model for palliative care was born.

The Sisters offered us a house in the residential section of Nsambya Hospital which was in between the nursing school and the hospital. The house is known as the VMM (Volunteer Missionary Movement) house as it was built from a gift from a VMM nurse working at the hospital. Our neighbours were Dr Pius Olkon and his family on one side and the Nursing Tutor, Catherine Owollu on the other. Catherine was then the Nurse Tutor at Nsambya Mission Hospital, and was to join hospice some years later as our Nurse Advocate with the Ministry of Health.

Figure 8.1 *Nsambya VMM House, 1993, our first home, where we saw patients in the front room.*

The house had two bedrooms and we saw the first 'walk in' patients in the lounge of the house where we ate and rested. There was one particular patient who would arrive at 6.30 am. This man, a retired teacher, wasn't in severe pain physically but was suffering from depression and was seeking counselling. It is very difficult when you're in palliative care to turn anyone away at any time, even if they come while you're still asleep in bed!

Meanwhile I was learning how to live in a Ugandan compound. We were given two chickens by a kind friend in Masaka, meant of course for eating. Later we were given a white turkey from a grateful family, again meant for eating. . . But I cannot kill or eat any live thing that I have looked in the eye – meat needs to be anonymously packed in Tesco's! (I have now got used to buying beef from the butcher who has the cow complete with head and hooves hanging about the wooden *duka* – a small shop – where he is selling the meat.)

The chickens and the turkey would come home every evening and take up residence in our larder and sleep there for the night. I noted that the neighbours also had chickens who all knew which house they belonged to and arrived at the back door at the same time!

Occasionally Turkey Lurkey was late. He was courting another turkey in the compound. Then I had to go looking for him and bring him home under my arm, much to the glee of the local people (patients and staff) who delighted at the *m'zungu* turkey being taken home by the *m'zungu*![13]

The consultants and doctors of Nsambya started to refer us patients from the ward. The nurses became very interested and involved and would ask the doctors to let us see the patients who were in pain. We were also teaching in the nursing school so the nursing students could help provide advocacy to support hospice. From time to time we were given the opportunity to talk to the doctors at their weekly meeting.

After assessing and controlling pain and symptoms, most patients wanted to return to their own homes. Many for the first time realised how ill they were, because if they wanted to know, we would let them know their diagnosis and prognosis so that they could make plans for the life that was left. We would discharge these patients as soon as possible and follow them up in their own homes. Sadly, many of the patients that would be referred to us at the start of our work would die within a few hours because the medical staff did not understand our role and the need to see them from diagnosis if possible so that we could form relationships with the patient and family.

Rose Kiwanuka was one of the first nurses that we met in Nsambya Hospital; she was in charge of St Theresa's gynaecological ward in which there were a lot of women with cancer of the cervix. Rose still tells how she was attracted to our work because she felt so helpless with the amount of pain suffered in her ward and had no way to relieve it. But all of a sudden we arrived with the magic oral morphine and the skills of symptom control, and the patients were at peace.

*

Let me tell you about two patients we found in Rose's ward in Nsambya Hospital, Uganda.

---

[13] *M'zungu* is a word that has come to mean 'white person' in many Bantu languages of east, central and southern Africa. There are a number of variations depending on the location. Any light-skinned non-Asiatic person could be addressed as Mzungu/M'zungu in the region. (Wikipedia)

The first one referred was Margaret. She had cancer of the rectum, diagnosed five years previously, and was operated on leaving her with a colostomy. Sad to say, her partner with whom she had three children, left her when this happened – and it was especially sad as he was a doctor. She had managed her colostomy very well but was beginning to feel severe pain which was a combination of nerve and somatic pain.

Figure 8.2 *Margaret with a younger me!*

To complicate matters she was trying to run a small shop, a *duka*. She was only able to receive help from her niece. The partner that left her was sending school fees, but nothing for her personal care. We actually had this lady on a morphine pump (one of the five cases on a pump in the first two years) and her pain was controlled on this. But her biggest struggle was the emotional pain she was experiencing due to her partner's abandoning her. Despite his cruelty, Margaret kept his picture in her Bible and prayed for him to the day she died. She passed away three months after we first started seeing her. But due to the relief we gave her she was able to work in her shop up until the day of her passing.

The second patient, Florence, had a similar diagnosis but it had been made only five months previously. She was very poor and had three children. When she came to the hospital five months previously, they performed major surgery which also left her with a colostomy. Sadly, her husband also disappeared when he was confronted with the bill for the operation!

I was first called to see her in an outside room of the gynaecological ward. There were six beds in the ward. She had such a stench from her wound that the rest of the beds were empty because other patients refused to stay in the same room. She had swollen lymph glands which contained metastases from her cancer. This swelling had been incised, by a health worker, leaving her with a constant discharge and smell from the area. We were able to control the smell completely by using crushed metronidazole tablets and applying the powder to the wound.

She had terrible pain, was very thin and obviously had very little time left to live, so we were very anxious to get her back home to her children and mother. Her mother, Kevina, was already looking after nine orphans whose parents (her children) had all died from HIV/AIDS. Most of the children were not able to go to school.

Florence died within a few weeks of going home. Before she died she became extremely weak. The wound opened and the colostomy fell back into her abdomen. But despite this we were able to support her up to her death. We even continued to support the orphans with whom we have still kept in contact to this day.

These two patients taught us a valuable lesson. Why had Margaret lived for five years and Florence died so quickly? Florence's immune system was highly suppressed due to her HIV. The question presented was: 'Should people with HIV and low CD4 counts have surgery at all?' Could they be too weak to handle the operation and post op recovery? In which case was surgical intervention only bringing on more pain and a more uncomfortable death?

The problems facing the patient and those tending to them are of course compounded by the financial tragedy for the family trying to deal with steep bills which they are unable to pay. This often leads, as in the above cases, to the abandonment of the patient by the partner and/or the family.

9   Initial Support

The Lord has done great things for us
And we are filled with joy.
Psalm 126:3

IT IS VERY DIFFICULT starting a new initiative, especially when people do not understand where you're coming from and where you want to go.

Palliative medicine was a completely new concept in Uganda in 1993. However, supporters both from the medical and the lay community began to come forward once they understood the difference that palliative care could make for the individual patient and the community. People in Uganda who had written to us after the article was published in the journal, *Contact*, included Professor Ignatius Kakande, Head of the Department of Surgery at Makerere University, Professor John Sali, a surgeon who later became a board member and Dr Steven Opito, MD, from orthopaedic medicine who sadly died between the feasibility study and the commencement of Hospice Africa Uganda (HAU).

During our visit on the feasibility study we could tell that Dr Opito was very ill: he was severely emaciated, had a hacking cough and also confided in us that he had TB. In 1993, it was very common for people that you knew quite well to die. The AIDS epidemic was at its peak.

Another person who helped us very much initially was Philip Curtain. He was the Irish consul and always extended us a welcome at his office in Nsambya. Philip is an architect in the firm of Petefield & Bodgener. He helped by putting us in touch with motor mechanics and other necessary people to maintain equipment and building, so we would not lose money. He also applied for a grant on our behalf from the Irish government, for a house that could be converted into our own hospice building.

Professor Kakande had really worked hard on our behalf and he also put us in touch with Henry Mary Kateregga, who later became the Chairman of the Board. Henry, in 1993, was an entrepreneur businessman, who had some properties in Kampala and was the owner of the only Mercedes Benz in the country – in fact he owned three!

72

He was invaluable in helping us find sites for the hospice and places to live since we knew that our time in Nsambya Hospital was limited. He used to come and collect me in his two-seater Benz which was so smart and luxurious that I would feel very embarrassed driving out of the hospital compound with him. He loved looking at properties that were out of this world and that would have been impossible for us to have – but we looked at them all the same. One of them was on top of Tank Hill with a master bedroom the size of a church and a view out of Lake Victoria. I remember thinking there would be nothing left for me to enjoy in heaven if we had been able to afford that site.

After more trips with Henry Mary we found two houses for sale in Makindye, side by side. One of these was to become the main site for Hospice Africa in Uganda. The Irish government would pay for one house, while Henry Mary was really taken with the second one and would have had the means to buy it, but he was pipped at the post by a Ugandan lady. This lady was very interested in our work but sadly she too became very ill and died a couple years later. Eventually in 2001, this house became available after being rented out to a colonel in the Uganda Peoples Defence Force (UPDF). It was then bought and renovated for hospice, for the Distance Learning Diploma (DLD for Africa) by the Irish government. This house was named Fazal House after Mbaraka Fazal, the pioneering nurse who was with me at the start of hospice in Uganda.

We eventually found a four-bedroom house in Muyenga, which we rented, with the view to having the hospice service from this house doubling up as the residence, if we did not find an affordable or rich donor to provide the first hospice. This was before Henry Mary offered his house in Ndebba (the industrial area) rent-free for six months. The Muyenga house was too big for one or two residents but we used it to accommodate several donors. In those days there were very few places to stay in Kampala. So they stayed with us and learned about our vision. This spirit of hospitality, so essential to hospice, even continues today, as my home is still offered to volunteers and other supporters of hospice. Carrying on the service of hospitality is core to our spirit.

Henry had lent his house to the Sacred Heart Missionary Fathers, who had sought safety from Masaka during the troubles. Now they were returning because it had become safe again. So the hospice moved into this house in January 1994. This was a two-bedroom house on a small plot of land ringed by a wire fence. We were able to park the land rover in front of the house.

Figure 9.1 *This is me receiving the keys of our first HAU home,
now Merriman House, Makindye, 1994.*

Figure 9.2 *Rose Kiwanuka assists a patient to get home in the first Land
rover given by the BHC in 1993.*

Figure 9.3 *The then Board of Advisors. From left: Mr Mafidiri (board member), Professor Ignatius Kakande, Naomi Nasasira, Jane Kibirege, visitor, Mary Mukasa, Henry Ssentoogo, Martha Rabwoni (Nursing Sister), Micheal McGoldrick (Pharmacist); seated: Rose Kiwanuka. Second car donated by Survive Liverpool in 1995, following a tragic accident to their first land rover ambulance in 1994.*

During the time in Ndebba, some of the surgeons, including Dr Sam Zaramba, later to become Director of Medical Services in Uganda, introduced us to several Rotary clubs in Uganda. Sadly none of these Rotary clubs supported us. As I said previously, it is difficult for people to support a vision rather than work that is already happening on the ground. But this effort of preparing proposals, giving talks and spending time away from patients was to start a pattern with donors which continues even today. There is a need for our donors to understand our need to be with patients.

Starting up in 1993–94 we had no office equipment or facilities for photocopying, so proposal writing was a problem. The Lutheran World, an international charity, had an office in town and Martin Dillon, the Irishman in charge, was so helpful to us, allowing us to use the photocopier and his secretary to assist with proposal writing.

It is because of these experiences of getting a service off the ground that hospice has a heart for new organisations in other countries in Africa. Nowadays, we are able to give them some financial support and training both in their own countries and through the Model in Uganda. We were also privileged to offer a home to the African Palliative Care Association (APCA) for two years before it was able to obtain its own premises. During those two years, we supported the initiation, found a premises (which they now own) and gave financial support when the first conference nearly fell through because funding promised from the USA came too late to secure the hotel and conference facilities. The Palliative Care Association of Uganda (PCAU), commenced at HAU in 1999 and was supported by volunteers until funding came for their first office in 2006. They did tremendous pioneering work at that time and continue to do so today.

To go back to Professor Ignatius Kakande, he was a dedicated Christian and introduced us to his family. At that time his children were quite young and sang beautifully together. His wife Brigid, the first volunteer nurse to work with us, was particularly helpful with a case during Christmas 1993 which taught me a lot of personal lessons.

We were asked to see a child in the Orthopaedic Department. Bashir, aged eight, was of mixed parentage. His parents were in Tanzania, his father was Tanzanian and his mother was Ugandan. He had developed an osteosarcoma of the scapula and when we assessed him, he had already had a forequarter amputation. This means that they removed the arm and the shoulder.

We saw Bashir five days after the surgery and he was in severe pain. He had an enlarged liver which indicated that he already had metastases and that his prognosis was quite short. He was still receiving surgical dressings for his wound which had been skin grafted, so the surgeons wanted him to stay in hospital over Christmas. I had let Luke (our driver) and Fazal go home for Christmas so I was the only one on duty. On Christmas Eve they contacted me. Bashir was quite ill and the grandmother desperately wanted to get him home because she didn't want him to die in the hospital.

I drove in to see him. He had high fever and a diagnosis of malaria, for which he was being treated, and a very anxious granny begging for us to get him back to his home. Working through an eleven-year-old interpreter (John) who was a relative of another patient, we ascertained that the granny lived in Lugazi within 20 km of Mulago (I didn't know the geography at the time) and John agreed to come with us.

So we set off and drove to Lugazi. After about 60 km we took a side road and began to climb a mountain for 10 km, where there was no road. Granny only knew the road that she would walk on, hence the land rover made its own way. Bashir required dressings of his wounds at least twice a week and we were now committed to helping him.

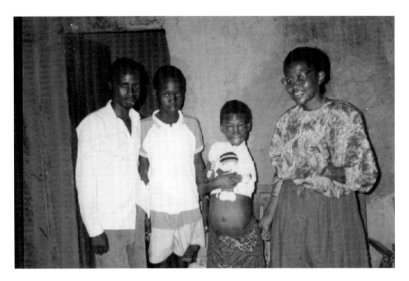

Figure 9.4 *Our first volunteer Nurse, Mrs Brigid Kakande, at home with Bashir 1993.*

Mrs Brigid Kakande joined the Christmas spirit and came with me every time. We visited him twice a week until he died six weeks later and the visit would usually take all day. Bashir was always glad to see us coming, and in order to prevent pain for him while changing his dressings we gave him a prior dose of morphine. The local community also looked forward to seeing the *m'zungu* arriving. Imagine how Bashir would have died if we hadn't been there with the magic morphine.

The lessons that I learnt from this were as follows:

1. It is difficult for people in rural areas to estimate distances.
2. God helps you to go the extra mile.
3. Even the steepest of mountains can be climbed if the end result is going to bring relief to the patient.

Many of the early patients remain vividly in my mind. We actually had a Christmas party in the nurse training school that year and we had ten patients attend. Many of the patients taught us about the culture and the expectations. I was on a steep learning curve, learning from my team, Ugandan patients and friends, the cultural rituals surrounding death and into bereavement.

The thing that really struck me most was that in Africa, by the age of 20, they have seen so many people dying in the family. Ugandans accept dying as part of life. Their cultural rituals taking people into bereavement ensure support for a fixed time. Because of poverty, people can't sit around and cry. They have to take care of the children, feed the family, and look after the farm. In my childhood it used to be said that time was a great healer. But time without work can be destructive as we often see in our own culture. Cultural aspects were learned from the patients and our teaching sessions. Because of the different tribes that make up Uganda there was a lot of sharing of our cultural knowledge during our courses.

But every patient was so grateful for anything we did to comfort their pain. When outsiders come to look at our work they often say we must be stressed out, but I always remind them that in our field we have a joy that no other medical specialty receives. This is a very special time of life and we are privileged to share it with the patient and the family. The Ugandans are deeply spiritual and share their grief, sorrows and their gratitude.

We also learned with our first patients that they do not want many people attending their needs during this time. Our nurses have to be a combination of all specialties. In the training for nurses as well as pain and symptom control we include counselling, attending to activities of daily living (occupational therapy), spiritual needs, social needs and developing networking with sister organisations that can support social needs for the patients.

Shortly after we went to live in Muyenga, a lady appeared at our home one day to ask me if I could help her father who had just returned from the UK, having had radiotherapy for cancer of the oesophagus. He was very uncomfortable and in a lot of pain. She had relatives staying next to the house where I was staying. We began to look after him and he regained so much strength he was able to return to his farm in Mbarara. His farm was his life and several times when we went to follow him up, we would have to go out to the fields and examine him in front of the cows.

He was still taking morphine and at the same time was deciding which bull would mate with what cow. He continued living with his wife on his farm until, several years later, he passed away. His daughter, Naomi Nasasira, was really touched by the work that was being done by hospice. She became a founder member of the Board of Trustees and served until 2008. Recently she has been appointed the Ugandan representative for the Hospice Africa Foundation.

*

Early in 1994 it was important that a constitution was written and a board was formed so that Hospice Africa Uganda could be registered as an NGO in Uganda. The following year we were also registered as a company limited by guarantee. This is an essential move, so that if the charity became bankrupt any financial responsibilities would not fall on board members. The first board consisted of Naomi, Henry Ssentoogo, Henry Mary Kateregga, Philip Curtain, Professor Kakande and myself.

While in Nairobi, I had learned a very special lesson in regard to board and management and motivation. By law the board of directors legally controls the organisation and its policies. Bureaucracy is anathema to the hospice concept. Hence it is important that when you go into a new country, with a new concept and a new and different ideology, the initial board should be called a board of advisors because as advisors they can advise us but we don't have to take their advice. This gives an organisation time to engage the board with the ethos. Looking back, I can see that I may have failed in seeing that every board member had mentoring and proper infusion of the ethos. This has led to many problems further down the line and even today. But on the whole the board has been great and very supportive.

Henry Mary had been a great teacher for many years and was well known in Masaka district for his talent. During the troubles, he became a refugee in Kenya, where he continued to teach in a Catholic school in Nairobi. During that time, he invested in his skills and became quite a clever business man. When he returned to Uganda he continued with his newly acquired skills and was again successful.

In 1995, Henry's health began to take a turn for the worse. Normally, very solid in stature he began to reduce to a fraction of his original size. We were all worried about him as we saw his state deteriorate progressively from meeting to meeting. Just before Christmas he became seriously ill and we would go to visit him at his home in Natete, a suburb of Kampala, where he was on bed rest.

In January 1996 I was on retreat at Namugongo when they informed me that Henry had died. I rushed back for the funeral. His death deeply upset me for he was such an amazing man with such a generous spirit and had done so much to help hospice get off the ground. May he rest in peace.

However I was very disillusioned at the funeral. Henry had supported a political party and the man leading the party took advantage of the funeral of this 'big' man to preach his politics which went on and on. I avoid funerals except for the poor because this is a common platform for political speeches these days.

When we built our first residential house for students of palliative care, we named it 'Kateregga House' in honour of Henry. We also named the first comprehensive course in his memory, designed for people in other countries. This happened in 2000 and was our first training for another country in Africa, Tanzania.

The team

For the first few months I had been very much on my own. Fazal was going back and forth to Eldoret due to her father's death. In January 1994, we held our first course for health professionals at the Davies Lecture Theatre at Makerere Medical School. Among the health professionals attending was Rose Kiwanuka, the nurse in charge of the female surgical ward in Nsambya Hospital, and I asked Rose if she knew anyone dedicated enough to join us for our work. While she thought about it, we engaged a nurse who had experience with cancer patients. Sadly she left us within a month because, besides her salary, she had had other forms of funding in her previous job. It was common for nurses in the Government service to accept payment from the patient for their services. Shortly after this, Rose offered to come, and following a successful interview, she joined the team.

Our team was now growing as we engaged our first secretary, Betty, and our first general worker, Jackson, and Ishywishy the First, our Hospice Cat☺, soon to be joined by Wishy Washy the First (see picture opposite).

While in Ndebba, the First Secretary of the British High Commission, Mr Michael Frost, was very helpful to us. He was the person who negotiated the ten-year-old land rover and put us in touch with Jersey Overseas Aid, which assisted us in several capital projects over the next several years.

At that time another notable patient came to us from the Cancer Institute. This was Robert, aged twelve, who had a huge Burkitt's lymphoma[14] on the face. It failed the second round of chemotherapy so his prognosis was dim. He was staying in Gabba with his aunt because his family lived far from Kampala.

Figure 9.5 *First team with land rover, in Ndebba 1994; (from left) Jackson holding Ishywishy, Betty, Anne, Rose Kiwanuka and Luke.*

He slept under the counter in his aunt's shop. Once a week I'd bring him to hospice just so that he could have a change of scenery. This was the start of day care. As Robert got weaker he was unable to swallow. At that time, with a small team, every member of the team was involved in patient care. Betty, the secretary, would draw up a syringe of juice so he could sip on it.

---

[14] Burkitt's lymphoma first named by Dennis Burkitt (1911–1993), born in Enniskillen, a graduate of Trinity College Dublin, who was a Professor at Makerere University in Uganda. This tumour, at first associated with the malaria belt was later associated with the Epstein Barr virus. Dennis Burkitt was a missionary doctor who researched cancer in Africa in relation to disease and diet.

When I would go to collect Robert, there were at this time very large bumps and potholes on the road that would cause him a lot of pain. After his death the President of the United States, Bill Clinton visited Uganda, for which they levelled the roads so he wouldn't get a bump on his bum. The Roberts of this world do not count but presidents do. How sick is that?

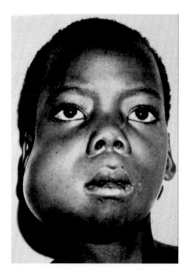

Figure 9.6 *An early picture of a child with Burkitt's lymphoma, looked after by Professor Dennis Burkitt.*

Figure 9.7 *Betty, our first secretary, helps Robert, at day care in Ndebba, 1994. The spirit of hospitality and sharing was for all the team.*

During the time we were looking after Robert, Mr Frost came out with a distinguished guest, Joan McAleish from the Scottish Catholic International Aid Fund (SCIAF). SCIAF was supporting our initial training programmes. That was the day that Robert usually came into hospice. At this stage Robert's tumour had broken though the skin, making a terrible sight. With his severe weight loss, the tumour appeared even larger and was beginning to erode into the neck.

We told Robert that he didn't need to come in that day, but he always loved to visit the hospice and insisted on coming. As Mr Frost and Joan arrived, the tumour eroded one of the major vessels in his neck and started to bleed heavily. Pressure bandages were able to stop the bleeding but Robert passed away that night. I think meeting Robert made a great impression on Mr Frost and Joan. SCIAF supported us all the way up to 2000, and the British High Commission supports us on and off, depending on the priorities of the present commissioner.

10 Challenges and Blessings of Colleagues and Governments

We have to allow ourselves to be open to pain ...
If we are able to do this, to act, as it were, as blotting paper ...
without handing it on in a form of bitterness
and resentment or of hurt to others –
then somehow in some incomprehensible miracle of grace,
some at least of the darkness may be turned to light.[15]

IN 1963 WHEN I was receiving my qualifications for medicine I was taught like everyone else in that day that Class A drugs like pethidine, morphine and heroine are addictive and should not be used, or should be used very sparingly while practising medicine. There was no special teaching about pain or its management. Many doctors of the old school were not aware of continuing medical education (CME) and were not aware of the recent advances taking place in the world. The 'old school' doctors are very powerful in most countries. These doctors did not and do not take it well when somebody says it is now a human right to be free from pain and talks about the use of morphine.

I have found this problem when bringing palliative care to Singapore, Kenya, Uganda and we continue to find it today in the countries in Africa where we are introducing palliative care. The fact that most of these elders in medicine are male compounds the problem. In Africa in particular, some men are even more dominant than in the rest of the world and don't take well to a female doctor bringing in a new specialty!

Difficulties with colleagues can be immediate (such as with the doctors with whom you work every day) or remote and distant (such as with people you may be working with on international policies). Even today in Uganda, considered to have the best palliative care in Africa, there are consultants who refuse to allow their patients' pain to be controlled with oral morphine, even though sometimes these patients are

---

[15] M. Spufford, *Celebrations*, Collins, London, 1986.

their own colleagues. They are prepared to watch them as they die in pain and misery.

This is really very sad and getting through to senior colleagues has been difficult in every country.

However in Uganda in 1998, we were lucky enough to be able to take on board a senior doctor who at the time was Chairman of the Drug Authority. Dr Jack Jagwe is one of the most respected physicians in Uganda and has in the past been director of Mulago Hospital, a teacher of almost every doctor that has come through Makerere, and has held a senior position in the Ministry of Health.

Dr Jagwe came on board as our Senior Advisor in National Policy in 1998. His work with the Uganda government resulted in palliative care being stated as an essential clinical service for all Ugandans in the strategic National Health Plan, 2000–05. This statement came solely from the concern for AIDS and not cancer. AIDS in fact has had a spin-off in bringing palliative care into the public arena. Cancer which causes severe pain is not among the top ten causes of death in Uganda and in most African countries. The top ten causes of death are almost always infectious diseases and infections are more common in immuno-suppressed HIV patients.

Dr Jagwe's advocacy with senior colleagues has been an incredible assistance in moving the barriers to morphine in Uganda and other African countries.

*

Uganda was a relatively easy country to advocate for affordable morphine. Dr James Makumbi, the Minister of Health in 1993, was very aware of the suffering from cancer and AIDS in Uganda and agreed readily to powdered morphine being imported. However, the big problem came with the people who filled out the paperwork for the importation of morphine. I am sure these people did not take kindly to my audacity in trying to expedite the documentation required. There was still a lot of uncertainty and even fear of criminalisation around its use.

But the morphine was available within six months and we were able to start the service in September 1993. However, we did not make much progress with the rest of the Ministry of Health until 1998 when Dr Jagwe came on board. And in fact our reception at the MoH was often as frosty as it can get in a tropical climate!

It was in 1998 when I first experienced rejection from a senior person in the Ministry of Health. After sitting outside his door for some hours, Rose Kiwanuka and I having been assured by his PA that he would see us, he appeared at the door and a cloud passed over his face. We were asked to wait outside and when we returned a tearful PA told us he would not see us. This same senior person had the grace to apologise to us some years later, now convinced that we are assisting the suffering of AIDS patients and cancer.

Singapore was a different story. In 1985, when we first began promoting palliative care medicine the country already had powdered morphine and most other analgesics needed and available at the time. The problem had nothing to do with morphine but with the concept of hospice care. As I have already mentioned, there is a famous road in Singapore called Sago Lane, which housed 'death houses'. Often the Chinese considered it unlucky to die in their own house so as death approached they were transferred to a 'death house'.

The care at these places was absolutely minimal and, as I have said, the poor person was on a roller coaster to the graveyard via the undertaker who worked next door! These houses were closed under the governance of Prime Minister Lee Kuan Yew, as they were thought to be, and indeed were, a scandal. But the belief remained that hospice equated with death houses. So we were actually getting nowhere with the government until 1986 when WHO published their bestseller *Cancer Pain Relief*.[16] This indicated that although we had the knowledge of pain control since 1967 many people throughout the world, in both the developed and developing world, were still suffering terribly from pain. This publication was sent to the Ministries of Health throughout the world and in Singapore it fell on fertile soil. The Minister of Health had lost his sister just a year before, in terrible pain from cancer. He now realised that this should not have happened, so he called a meeting of all those involved in pain and palliative care (we had just commenced home care and were working with St Joseph's Home for the aged which had opened twelve beds for patients of all ages in need of palliative care) and there we discussed pain control as stated in the WHO book.

This was quite an argumentative meeting. Among the controversies, one of the anaesthetists present was adamant that oral morphine could not control pain and should not be used in Singapore. When I confronted him with our own experience, he stated that he had been trained in the

---

[16] World Heath Organisation, *Cancer Pain Relief*, WHO, Geneva (1986).

famous pain centre at Walton Hospital in Liverpool! I was able to tell him that I was born within five miles of the centre and was in touch with them as well. In fact they had given us some PCA (patient controlled analgesia), computerised pumps, then in an early stage of development, for our use with our Singapore patients. So often we find that we come to blows over our pride and the issues are put on hold. But we had the answers ready that day.

The Minister was convinced that palliative care could be introduced to Singapore and after our volunteer group carried out home care from 1984, five years later home care services were incorporated into the health system. With a population of 2.5 million, it was relatively easy to commence in comparison to some of the countries in Africa: e.g. Nigeria with a population of 150 million and even Uganda with a current population of 33 million.

Back to Uganda, and as stated above, we were getting nowhere fast with the Ministry of Health up to 1998. However, through teaching the undergraduate medical students, most of whom were now doctors, and training the health professionals in practice, we were changing attitudes. But the converts needed the support of their seniors.

It was therefore planned in 1998 to hold an advocacy meeting, with all those involved, including the cancer and AIDS patients. We needed to bring to this meeting those who were in a position to make decisions which could change practice. We managed to obtain a grant from the Scottish Catholic International Aid Fund (SCIAF), who had been funding our education programmes, so that we could hire a hotel for this meeting. It was so expensive, but the VIPs would not come to a humbler place.

We invited the people from the National Drug Authority, the Ministry of Health, The AIDS Support Organisation (TASO), Mulago Hospital, medical schools at Makerere University and Mbarara University of Science and Technology (MUST) and there were in all about forty attendees. In spite of our advocacy at the Ministry of Health, they decided to send a junior minister who was a dentist. However he, with the others, was enthused by our guest speaker, Dr Jan Stjernsward, who had previously been Head of Cancer and Palliative Care in WHO Geneva. With a background of oncology and work in Kenya, he was an ideal person, with a great fire in his belly to convert the participants. It was he who suggested that we take Dr Jagwe on board as our part-time Senior Advocate, and he also managed to find the funding for him to commence the same year. Dr Jagwe was ideal because of his position of Chair of the National Drug Authority. We have found him such a humble person to work with, yet he is firm in promoting what he believes and has moved the use of morphine not only in Uganda but in five other African countries.

This conference in 1998 was a landmark. It resulted in the Ministry of Health agreeing to have a palliative care steering committee to look into the needs of patients in Uganda. However, there was a stipulation that no expatriates were to be on this committee. This meeting, chaired by Dr Jagwe, culminated in palliative care being incorporated into the Health Strategic Plan in 2000. Since then the Ministry of Health in Uganda has been very cooperative about the needs for palliative care. In 2001 with the recommendation of Cecilia Sepulveda from the Department of Cancer and Palliative Care in WHO Geneva, a country team was established with all the players having a representative on board. This still exists today, although not as active as we would like.

This group, with Dr Jagwe and the Commissioner of Health Services, Dr Jacinto Amandua, taking a leading role, managed to have the statute allowing midwives to prescribe pethidine, changed to include allowing nurses and clinical officers, trained in Hospice Uganda for nine months, to now prescribe morphine, thus increasing our prescribers. It took two years for this to go through parliament, but we are still the only country allowing this in Africa, although several other countries are trying to change their own statutes to increase prescribers.

Figure 10.1 *A child waits for the team to finish with her mother. She is being kept from school to care for her.*

Increasing the prescribers

Nurses are the backbone for palliative medicine in most countries. This is even more so in countries short of doctors such as we find in Africa. The training of medical students and student nurses is a priority in palliative medicine so services can be available to the sick of the future. Thus it is important to bring advocacy to major medical schools and other schools of health professionals in the country.

In most countries the only prescribers for Class A drugs are doctors, vets and dentists. Of these, it is usually only doctors who prescribe morphine for cancer pain. Because of the economic situation in every country there is a constant brain drain as the educated seek career opportunities and increased salaries elsewhere. The doctor to population ratio in Africa varies from 1:4000 to 1:100,000 (in the UK it is 1:450).

To make the situation worse, many of these doctors are behind desks in the government or ministries instead of practising medicine. The majority of practising doctors are in the big cities so their children can go to good schools and they have access to the most modern amenities.

In villages doctors are rarely seen, except when attached to district hospitals. However, in some countries, such as Tanzania and Malawi, clinical officers, the cadre of health professional between doctor and nurse, are allowed to prescribe class 'A' drugs. In Uganda clinical officers are still not allowed to prescribe. But, as stated, with the advocacy of Dr Jack Jagwe from HAU and Dr Jacinto Amandua, from the Ministry of Health, the government now allows nurses and clinical officers trained for nine months at a registered course at HAU to be official prescribers on completion of the course.

There is a rapid way to increase prescribers, if we could have a 'rapid prescribers' course' for clinical officers. This could double our prescribers overnight and is being discussed with the Ministry of Health at the moment.

Networking organisations

It is important to know what is on the ground before going into another country to start a service and links need to be made with other organisations that can increase access to those in need, as well as allowing integration of care. Dealing with governments in other countries was difficult in that every country has a different culture. It is always good to have somebody on the ground who is in good standing with the government and who would know the necessary people and arrange appointments on one's arrival (see Chapter 22). We experienced many obstacles entering new countries when we first started to work in African countries with the aid provided by the Diana Fund in 2000–03.

For example, when we first came to Uganda, TASO and several other support organisations were already supporting AIDS patients in the communities, but did not have the knowledge of pain and symptom control. Dr Mirian Duggan, a Franciscan Sister from Nsambya Hospital and founder of Nsambya Home Care, had the spirit of hospice and palliative care at her fingertips. However, in order to continue their supportive care till the end of life, the knowledge of pain and symptom control was essential. Over the subsequent years we have worked with these support organisations trying to graft palliative care on to their services. But palliative care is time-intensive – we need a lot of time to assess and to continue with patients who are critically ill or coming to the end of life.

Thus palliative care, if practised properly, does not increase numbers which many donors are looking for. The reason is that palliative care is like the intensive care unit of a hospital. You cannot have hundreds in such units at one time because we need to give intensive care. Our patients' conditions often change from day to day and they need their team to be able to talk to them at least on the phone, and visit when necessary. However, a model of what is possible can be seen at Kitovu Mobile in Masaka. Palliative care has been grafted on to this service by Dr Carla Simmons, MMM, giving time for the patient, and has even been extended not only to AIDS patients but also to cancer patients in the area.

It is recommended that a palliative care team is separate from the overall support team in these organisations. Advocacy is so important with networking organisations. Rivalry occurs regularly due to competition for donors. It can become bitter and detrimental to the patients and families when organisations start putting each other down to donors.

Within the hospice ethos, we try to recognise that there are many people in need and we are all needed. However palliative care needs to be considered separately by both networking organisations and donors. Many donors are depending on numbers seen, but donors for palliative care organisations need to realise that it will never be comparative to support organisations. In more recent years, collaboration with networking organisations has increased greatly; many of our patients are receiving antiretrovirals (ARVs) from networking organisations and only need us when in pain or with a critical illness. Palliative care is recognised as a need for AIDS patients by most AIDS organisations today. But there was quite a resistance to recognising this for many years which made it difficult for us. The Mildmay Centre for Palliative Care of HIV/AIDS Patients commenced care for HIV/AIDS in 1998 from a different angle with their state-of-the-art building and provided care from diagnosis to death. However, they were not doing home care and today they refer patients to our hospice service as we do to them for those requiring ARVs and family support.

Pharmacists

Pharmacists need to be taken on board early in palliative care. In Uganda, they are very powerful within the Ministry of Health and also because there are so few they can demand very large salaries, even more so than doctors. Although we have taught occasionally in the school of pharmacy it has still not been taken into part of their curriculum. They still often teach the ancient teaching about Class A drugs. Pharmacies have their own professional organisation which sets the rules for dispensing. Therefore it is most important that links are made with the schools of pharmacy and with the pharmacists, particularly with those in the Ministry of Health, to ensure that these medications are available throughout the country and are included in the essential drugs list in the country. We have had great support in bringing morphine to the Districts of Uganda from their special pharmacist, Dr Fred Sebusubi.

We are not yet up to scratch with the pharmacists in Uganda and this needs to be addressed in the coming years.

In the Blue Book, our reference pocket book on palliative medicine in Uganda and other African countries, we have a list of 21 essential medications required for pain and symptom control. A second list of 22 medications, mainly antibiotics, is given for the management of opportunistic infections in the AIDS patient. The formula for the making of oral morphine from powder using water and a preservative is also available in this book. The Blue Book is now also available in French, and both English and French editions can be downloaded from the HAU website (www.hospiceafrica.or.ug).[17]

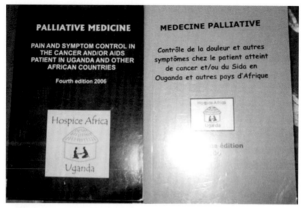

Figure 10.2 *The Blue Book in English and French has brought palliative medicine treatment affordable in Africa to many countries.*

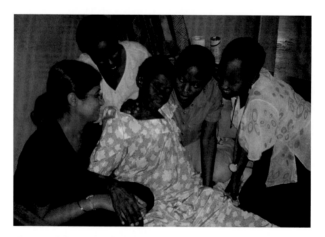

Figure 10.3 *Medical students from Makerere, on mobile rounds assisting a patient during a home visit.*

---

[17] Hospice Africa Uganda, *Palliative Medicine: the Management of Pain and Symptoms in Uganda and Other African Countries for the Cancer and AIDS Patient*, 4th edition 2006, French edition 2007.

11 The Birth of Mobile Hospice Mbarara and Little Hospice Hoima, 1998

In out of the way places of the heart,
Where your thoughts never think to wander,
This beginning has been quietly forming,
Waiting until you were ready to emerge.[18]

WE DID NOT intend to plant hospices under the name of Hospice Africa. Through the creation of a model that is affordable, culturally acceptable and adaptable to other conditions in African countries, we would assist other hospice and palliative care initiatives so that palliative care will eventually be available everywhere to those in need. So why did we commence two more hospices of our own in 1998?

We had been teaching the medical students of Makerere since 1993 and there were more and more doctors coming out every year, who now understood our work and supported the palliative care nurses. Mbarara University of Science and Technology (MUST) was the second medical school. After visiting in 1995, we realised that this school, which was established with the vision of having doctors trained in Uganda who would be available in the communities throughout the country, was crying out for such training to carry forward palliative care to rural areas. Mbarara, about 280 km south-west of Kampala and three hours forty minutes' drive, was therefore one of the sites we chose to visit with a view to setting up a rural hospice.

The other rural site we considered was Hoima, about 200 km north-west of Kampala and two hours forty minutes' drive. This was a very poor area with few services for cancer or HIV/AIDS. We needed a model that would start from scratch with nothing and be capable of visiting patients in a low density area.

There were several spin-offs for us in Kampala from our visits to the two sites. We received support and friendship from those we stayed

---

[18] John O'Donohue, *Benedictus*, op. cit., p. 33, for a new beginning.

93

with, all with prayer for the work and many with other assistance. In Mbarara our special friends included the Poor Clares, an amazing community of mainly Uganda women who were following the rule of St Francis and St Clare, praying, running a farm and healing the local community. They have been a home from home for me and the many friends I bring to Mbarara. The White Fathers in Mbarara and in Hoima have assisted us and Father Jim McTiernan was our special chaplain in the early years at Mobile Hospice Mbarara (MHM).

Father Charlie and the de Montfort Fathers assisted us with hospitality and practical support. Oliver Murphy and his wife Margaret who died in 2000 were great supporters all along. Oliver, now heading for 90, is supporting many schoolchildren, paying their fees in Mbarara. Mary Moran, while running her own training institute in Mbarara, helped us so much in the early days with practical assistance from her trainees. Nowadays we receive hospitality in Hoima from the Cistercian Sisters who have a small school near to the Trade School. Without these friends all these satellite programmes would not have moved. Thank God for them all.

Little Hospice Hoima (LHH) and Mobile Hospice Mbarara (MHM) are today more models for other African countries than the founding hospice in Kampala. In Kampala we are now a large compound with five buildings and more than 80 team members. It is a one-off but a centre of excellence and of training for all Africa.

When demonstrating a model for Africa we bring our visitors to visit MHM or LHH.

Mobile Hospice Mbarara

In 1995, we were invited to Mbarara to run a programme for health professionals, including the medical students at Mbarara University of Science and Technology (MUST). Up to then we had been taking our training programmes to districts on invitation and holding them regularly in Kampala. The numbers attending were kept to forty. However in Mbarara, we were loaned a lecture theatre which held more than 100 and we found that we had 70 attending most days. There was a mixture of attendees including the medical staff from the Mbara University Teaching Hospital (MUTH), several from the medical school and medical students as well as spiritual advisors, psychologists etc.

Figure 11.1 *MHM Team in 1999 with VSOs Brian and Clare Fitzgibbon with Dr Karen Frame.*

The District Health Officer showed interest in bringing such a service to the people of Mbarara. The University Vice Chancellor had been alerted to our training programmes in Makerere Medical School and invited us to teach the medical students in Mbarara. We submitted a curriculum and started ad hoc teaching when we were in Mbarara and from this began several years of meeting people in Mbarara and trying to raise local interest and funds. We made several friends in Mbarara who are with us to this day. They included the present Mayor of Mbarara, Wilson Tumwine and the Vice Chancellor, Professor Federic I. B. Kayanja the University Academic Registrar, Mr Stephen Bazirake and several others from the University. Local service clubs joined our meetings, held in a room at Wilson's Hotel.

Professor Pat Pathak, the Professor of Obstetrics and Gynaecology in MUST for some years and an International Rotarian, was leaving. He was internationally renowned as a Rotarian and had done a lot of work for India, where he was born, and other developing countries. He had been given a land rover by the Rotarians in UK to enable him to do outreach clinics in Mbarara. He had a driver, Hassan, and when he was leaving he was very keen that Hassan should have a good job and that the land rover would be used for humanitarian work. When he got to know about our moving towards a palliative care service in Mbarara, he approached us, promised us the car and asked us to take on Hassan as the first driver. He also gave us lots of medical sundries which he had stored in the university for our work. This was a great start.

But Pat did not stop at that: he began moving towards an application to International Rotary for a 3H grant. This is one of the largest grants given from Rotary International and we were indeed delighted when his application was accepted. The conditions of the grant were:

1. It would be used for service fitting in with the humanitarian aims of the 3H grant.

2. The local Rotarians would raise 10% of the amount requested.

3. That the local Rotarians would be involved in the application of the grant and that reports to Rotary International would come through the local Rotary club.

Condition (2) appeared to be out of the question for the local Rotarians in a developing world, so we managed to obtain the $25,000 required for a $250,000 grant, seeking help from the Rotarians of Coventry in UK where we had had a relationship since I worked in Birmingham in 1992. Hospice Africa contributed as did Pat's own Rotary club in Stockport, Lancashire.

The local Rotary did not contribute. However, they came in big time for the third condition and we formed a small committee for the handling of the grant with three Rotarians and four of our local friends, including Wilson, a local dentist, Dr Edwin Mugume, local vet, Dr Bernard Maniraguha, a member of the Lions International Club, Ms Gudo Alamira, Mr Charles Tushabomwe Kazooba, an accountant from the university, Martha, Hellen and Jackson, the first HAU members of the MHM team and myself. It was a difficult time for the fledgling hospice. The grant was for three years and the group met monthly initially, and later quarterly. This was my first time in Uganda to meet bureaucracy head on.

Figure 11.2 *Wilson Tumwine helped us with rooms for meeting and as a Member of Trustees, 1997; now Lord Mayor of Mbarara.*

It was not easy for the small team which was trying to get off the ground. In the end there was a delay of two years before the final package of the grant was agreed on. We had been diligent in meeting the conditions of the grant, marking our equipment in the hospice to make it clear that it had all come from Rotary and submitting all the reports on time.

The last instalment of the grant actually reached us four years after the first in 2003. Several times we came all the way from Kampala (280 km on a bad road) to find that the members had not turned up for the meeting without any notice or apology. The faithful members of our own selection started not to turn up as so many times they had wasted their precious time and we had had to cancel the meeting.

At the end of the grant, we were able to disband this Committee as MHM came under the Board in Kampala. But this was the 'crack' through which the light gets in and we learnt a lot from this experience. I have to say here that I have worked with Rotary clubs in many places in the world and relationships were always cordial until this time. Also the other members of the Board remain faithful to us to this day and attended our tenth year celebrations in 2008.

Apart from the financial and board problems, the hospice in Mbarara grew from strength to strength. Because the first car from Professor Pat Pathak was for a mobile clinic, it was decided to call the new project, Mobile Hospice Mbarara. The first office was in the new residence of the female medical students. We had two rooms there. We were also given the first house inside the gate of the residential compound for residential staff, rent free. Martha initially stayed there, keeping it warm for Brian and Clare, VSOs from UK. By the time Brian and Clare arrived, the rooms in the residence had been taken back and the hospice had moved to the garage of the house where Brian and Clare were to live. Later we were given rooms in the nursing school on the hospital compound.

We started to look for a property that we could buy and possibly renovate for a small hospice and found a house just after the turn onto the Fort Portal Road. It was in poor condition, partly built but being used as accommodation for local workmen, where they slept several to a room in the three-bedroom house. This belonged to a politician related to the President. But our hopes of special treatment from a rich and influential man were dashed and we had to cough up the full amount.

Brian, then the administrator, was making many local contacts on the golf course, and he managed to get a contractor who renovated it for the small team. At that time there were only six in the team – Hassan the driver and his wife, Amina Bukenya our housekeeper, Martha Rabwoni, my second nurse at HAU Kampala who now led the team with Jackson the accounts clerk, and two more nurses, Hellen Iyekat and Harriet Kebirungi. The numbers of patients were increasing. We were then joined by our first doctor, Dr Andrew Ndamira, and Dr Sheila Baingana gave us teaching and clinical sessions from her work in the department of medicine at MUST.

Daily the team would be called to the hospital for very ill patients. This was the era when HIV was at its height and there were many patients coming for assistance. Also there were very few ARVs, which were available only to the rich. Antifungals and even antibiotics were not available for the intercurrent infections and we saw so many sad cases in Mbarara from the villages where young mothers died followed by the new born deprived of the life-sustaining breast milk. When a patient was in the dire straits of low CD4 count, they would stumble from one infection to the next and from one pain to the next. It was so sad to see.

But the little team were well versed in the management of such patients and up to today have a very high standard care for all their patients and many of them are working overtime to ensure the comfort of patients.

The education programme commenced almost immediately and mirrored much that had been tried and proven essential in Kampala. The university teaching came on very quickly with nurses on degrees joining with the medical students on the palliative care programme. As the new millennium approached, links were forged with the Department of Medicine. Dr Karen Frame was over from the UK with her husband Dr Laurence John supported by THET (the Tropical Health Education Trust). Karen came to hospice on a regular basis and taught us all many things, including the generosity of spirit that that both she and Laurence brought to Mbarara.

They were there when the Ebola virus struck in the North with death in its wake. When one case was proved in Mbarara, an army man who had travelled, the hospital opened two wards, one male and one female for Ebola patients. The doctor designated to the wards was Laurence: he bravely took this on knowing that already one doctor had died in Gulu. Karen and Laurence went home and returned to us in Kampala, as Karen took over the Distance Learning Diploma from Michelle McGannon. By this time they had a son, Luke, a lovely little red-headed boy who charmed us all. Karen is still our link with THET in the UK. This year the diploma has been upgraded to a degree. We have been supported with a DFID (Department for International Development) grant coming through THET. Karen is a key person for us in the UK for this grant together with HA (UK).

As the teaching and the patient numbers increased there was a need to add onto the initial building, and a lecture hall cum day care room was added with offices in between. Under the large lecture room three bedrooms were put in where visiting hospice staff or visitors could be accommodated. VSO built a round traditional thatch-roofed house at the gate and this was used for meetings or for the guards and drivers.

New initiatives commenced in Mbarara. With the help of Clare Fitzgibbon, our VSO Macmillan nurse, the outreach commenced and the roadside clinics. Both of these have been extended to other hospice services in and out of Uganda. The outreach commenced with Ibanda, a hospital service about 75 kms from Mbarara with the team going for the day. However some patients are outside the catchment area for MHM but live en route to Ibanda so they were met under the nearest mango tree or another mutual place to meet and would be examined in the car and given their medications. If they were too sick to reach the meeting place, they were visited at home. In the early years, not so many had mobile phones but nowadays most know of someone who can call and tell us when such a patient is sick. We also have a note of their contact, which enables us to keep in touch. This is throughout the three hospices.

Over the years, friends from the sites of roadside clinics have given the use of a room, a clinic or church building to meet patients on the way and this has assisted the team greatly. The service became very much part of the community and at the tenth anniversary in 2008, many of the local people came forward to talk and relate their happier experiences with hospice caring for their loved ones. The Vice Chancellor of the University together with some of the original Board members came and some of the team members who had moved on came back to celebrate with us. This was after our walk through the streets of Mbarara, with a band, had alerted the local people that we had something to celebrate. As usual we had many followers who just came for the T-shirt and for food. The youngest is pictured here.

Figure 11.3 *The youngest walker at the Tenth Anniversary walk.*

MHM today

Today, MHM brings training programmes to the surrounding districts, the patients have increased greatly and in fact there is hardly room at hospice to admit any more staff to look after our patients. So today we are in the process of seeking funds to put up another education unit and then patient care facilities on the same site. The land has been donated by the Catholic Archdiocese of Mbarara and this has assisted us greatly. The site is a little further out from the hospital and university on the road to Kabale but we can reach the hospital by car in eight minutes. The funding for the building is being sought by HATN (Hospice Africa the Netherlands) under the leadership of Joan Kelly, an early volunteer with Hospice in Kampala, now Mrs Ronald Scheer, married to an honourable Dutch man!

It is impossible to mention all the special people in Uganda and from without, who visited MHM and worked alongside it to support it. Phil Moloney taught in the Mission school with the Daughters of Mary and Jesus (DMJ) Sisters and Brid Quinn nursed in Mbarara health centre, they both were out as Irish volunteers with APSO and still raise funds in their own groups in Ireland to support Martha and her team. The APSO volunteers who were in Uganda have been very faithful to HAU after their return to Ireland and their regular lives.

Mbarara opened on 6 January 1998, and is going from strength to strength. They presently have 342 patients on their programme and work with the networking organisations for the patients and are united with the local branch of the Palliative Care Association of Uganda.

A day in the life of a Mobile Hospice Mbarara nurse
by Martha Rabwoni

Martha was our second nurse at HAU in Kampala in 1994. In 1998, she took up the post of Health Services Coordinator at MHM. She is with the patients daily.

Dear Lord it's early, I am awake and tired. This is the best and worst time of my day.

It is 5 am and I have to prepare breakfast and the children for school. Jane is eight years old in Primary 3 and John is ten years old in Primary 5.

We will all come back late but the children will come back earlier than me so they will collect the milk for their tea and start preparing the supper. They are woken up and shown what to do when they come back in the evening.

I arrive at hospice, share greetings with colleagues and yesterday's experiences and events. Then the bell goes for prayers. We all meet to dedicate our day to the Almighty and share information. The education team tells us that they are going to Masaka and they will not be with us for the next one week. The Clinical Head announces that the mobile clinic will take place on Wednesday.

A visiting doctor from Mbarara Regional Hospital is requesting to come with us on the mobile clinic. Then we all go for teabreak and start our journey for the hospital and home visit, with one person remaining at hospice.

Today I am on Kabale Road and there are four patients to visit. Hadija is a patient with CA (advanced cancer of the cervix) with VVF (vesico vagina fistula); she is a widow and she has six children She has two sets of twins, almost the same age as my own children, and two singletons. They are really doing well in school but their mother is dying. Soon they will be shared among the family and they will miss each other.

The next patient lives up on the hill and the car might not be able to cross the bridge; it has to be left behind and we walk almost half a kilometre. She is a patient with cancer of the breast. Her pain is well controlled on drugs; the stench from her tumour is gone completely and she is now very happy.

Figure 11.4 *Home visit: visiting a patient during the early days at MHM.*

After this I attend a man with cancer of the prostate. He is paraplegic and I need to change his catheter. It takes a bit of time because the wife is also not so well. I will have to ask the driver to assist me to turn and put him in position.

The last patient is an HIV/AIDS patient with herpes zoster on the face. She is now improving but still unable to see and the worst pain has gone; she is so grateful. The patients' prayers and thankfulness make my day, no matter how tired and frustrated I feel. At the end of the day I feel revived, strengthened and with more energy to continue the work of the Lord.

I am back at hospice at 4.30 pm and we have to take a drink because it is past lunch time. I write up the charts and prepare for the next day.

Then back home the children are very happy to see me and eager to share with me their school stories and we have to eat supper, do the washing up, there is homework to be done and all this will end up at around 11pm when we will all retire to bed.

Little Hospice Hoima (LHH)

LHH opened on 1 June 1998 for a very different reason. Hoima had been a neglected part of Uganda ever since their king had opposed the British rule before independence. This deprivation of services, roads etc. continued and when we arrived in Kampala and started to go up country, the road to Hoima was still one of the worst in the country. The car stumbled from pothole to pothole for 200 km. If it was rainy season there was the extra thrill of the skids and poor visibility. Sadly in our early days a whole matatu bus went into the river, bringing several doctors back from a wedding to Kampala and all were killed. This was a great loss for the medical confraternity and the people of Uganda. But it is one of many other accidents on that road over those years.

It was during the year before LHH opened that Hilary Elfick, then representing 'Voices for Hospice' in London came out to witness at first hand our work. It was after her trip to Hoima and seeing the road leading to patients that she wrote her inspiring poem (see above, pp. 19–20).

We went up to run a programme for health professionals in 1997. When going to a new district we made a preliminary visit to the District Medical Officer and the health workers in the District Health Headquarters, as well as the local hospitals, NGOs working with home care and particularly with PLWA (People Living With AIDS). We studied the population and the whole area to see the logistics of the area both for bringing in the participants and the future possibility of home care services. The purpose of the contacts was to find local leaders who might chair sessions and talk on certain sessions on local culture, will-making in the area and spirituality.

One of the local leaders we were advised to contact by several people we met was Dr Stella Tibumanye. Stella had a general practice in the town but was also the Minister of Health in the local Bunyoro Government (Bunyoro was the local tribe). She had been working in Nigeria in her earlier medical career and was now back settled in her home town. She was well known for her care for the suffering and especially the HIV sufferers. We visited Stella to invite her to chair a session but once she saw the programme, she immediately said that she would attend the whole programme. This was a big sacrifice for her as she would have to hand over her practice to someone else for the seven days of the programme.

Stella attended the course with many other local people. Meeting Point, a support organisation in the area, attended and two members in particular were so skinny that it was obvious that 'slim' disease was well and truly established in Hoima. There were still no ARVs available and one dreaded the worst for the prognosis. However I am glad to tell you that one of these ladies, Veronica, is now a large lady running 'Meeting Point'; having lived to see the arrival of ARVs she has responded so well.

There were many discussions and a great thirst for our care to be brought to Hoima. Stella led this and invited us to start a service in Hoima and suggested that our first service could be run from her practice in the town. Her practice was in a shop in one of the main streets, with a very small area, no running water or electricity. We trained her in the case sheets for assessment and she started to see patients and record them for the programme.

Many of our first team were Bunyoro, from the Hoima area. Rose, whose mother lived in Hoima, and I went up to assess the area and Betty Kasigwa, also from the area, offered to go up and be the first palliative care nurse.

Stella agreed for us to make a small area in the clinic which would fit a patient couch and a small medicine cupboard over the head of the patient, with very little room for the nurse. Luckily Betty was very slim, but I, a larger lady, had great difficulty squeezing in to examine a patient once they were up on the couch! This was the first Little Hospice Hoima and a welcome sign was put in the street outside Stella's surgery 'Welcome to Little Hospice Hoima'.

Figure 11.5 *(above) Dr Stella Tibumanye on borda borda on home visit.*

Figure 11.6 *(right) Team on steps of the Nile Special (beer) warehouse, Hoima; from bottom: Betty Kasigwa, Robert (driver), Stephen (general assistant) and Lucy (secretary).*

Home visits began immediately but they had to be done on a *borda borda*. These are motorcycles, originally designed as bicycles, which would carry travellers across the no man's land between borders of countries. These are still there at Malaba, the border crossing between Uganda and Kenya. So the *borda bordas* became part of the home care scene except once a month we would visit from Kampala in a car and go out to see the furthest patients in the car. Even then we would often have to leave the car and walk up to a kilometre to the home of the patients because there was no road in.

We had a few visitors in those early days. Jan Stjernsward was one of them, and was really touched by how we were offering a service in such tiny conditions. We tried to find a suitable little house to call our own and he offered to pay for such, but none could be found.

A year later, an offer came from the Catholic Bishop, the Rt Rev. Dr Deogratias Byabazaire. A sister from his health centre had been on our training programme. She had suggested that we use two of the rooms in Bujunbura health centre as a base for the palliative care. This was further out of town on the Catholic Hill but patients could reach it on bicycle taxis or the *borda bordas*. At that time the beautiful health centre was poorly attended and they had rooms. It was there that LHH commenced day care, and continues drop-in patients and home visits (still without a car). However in 2001, a car was donated from a Rotary Club in Victoria, Australia. This was arranged through a doctor colleague of mine, Osborn Viegas, one of the Asians forced to leave the country by Idi Amin in 1973, but still with a big heart for Uganda, who was Professor of Obstetrics and Gynaecology in the National University of Singapore during my time there. He had moved to Australia where he joined the Rotary. Now living back in Singapore, Osborn is one of many in Singapore who continue to assist and support our work.

A couple of years later, the health centre was booming and they needed the couple of rooms back. So Betty and company went into town to find a suitable place to rent. They eventually settled on a drinks warehouse with an advert of Nile Special, the local beer, across the outside. There was a team of five: Betty Kasigwa and Jerith Birakurtaki made up the nursing team, supported by the driver, Robert Kyomuhendo, general assistant, Steven Byaruhanga and Lucy Mijumbi, secretary. The team set about painting the warehouse, making new areas to see patients, an area to teach and an office where patients could be seen in private, and a small pharmacy. To get into it, you had to climb a set of wooden steps with no support on the side facing the road, a scary experience for me never mind a disabled person or a weak patient. But all managed it! The premises were on the main street and easily accessible for patients. Combined with the advert for Nile Beer, the mobile notice 'Welcome to Little Hospice Hoima' now appeared again!

The White Fathers, with whom we received hospitality each time we visited Hoima, had a trade school for boys and workshops covering motor mechanics, carpentry, contracting for buildings etc. They also had a brick factory which manufactured 'Hoima brick', known all over Uganda for its beautiful sandy colour, wonderful finish and durability. We had had Hoima contractors for the clinical building in Kampala and this was much admired. Now we raised funds to have our own free-standing hospice in Hoima to be built by the same contractors.

Brother Carl had been the architect of the building in Kampala and was the architect for this building also. This humble man ran the trade school and cycled everywhere even though he was 75. Sadly he died on the very road that he cycled up and down to work and into Hoima, before the new LHH was completed. He was an example to us all and we lost a dear friend.

One of the rooms in the new building is dedicated to Brother Carl and another, the clinical room, is the 'Stella' room after Dr Stella. The Library is dedicated to the memory of the Rev. Derek Palmer and his wife Cecily whose family sent a large donation for LHH after the Rev. Palmer's death. But the house itself was named after Bjorn Simensen. Bjorn is another inspiring person. Born in Norway and now in Uganda for more than 40 years, he came to hospice about twelve years ago and has served on the Board. From there he has assisted us with every Hospice Uganda building, giving his time freely to ensure that the contract work is carried out to the specifications and needs of our patients and families.

But first of all we had to get land. We spent many months looking at land for sale and eventually came upon land belonging to the d'Souza family and bought from them half an acre to place the hospice. This was eventually built and opened on 5 October 2005.

Over all these years, the AIDS patients at Hoima have always exceeded the cancer patients. But it had such a small population that the expected number of cancer patients was quite small – 1050 from the population of 350,000. The PLWA (People Living With AIDS) would be expected to be 70,000 and those requiring palliative care (full blown AIDS) would be 14,000 in 1998. We were running with a minute number of patients receiving our care compared to those estimated to be in need. However the number of those with AIDS requiring palliative care has reduced as the death rate has reduced drastically with the advent of ARVs. Yet in a poor district like Hoima there are still many not accessing them. We estimate that with the increase of the population to 400,000 and the reduced prevalence of 6.7% HIV in Uganda, those requiring palliative care in Hoima district are now 1340, not including those who present with neuropathic type pain as a complication of their ARV therapy. This is compared with a prevalence of cancer of 1200. HIV is reducing but cancer is increasing in all African countries.

However many in Hoima never attended a health worker and there was a great need for a service of friends who would visit or belong to each village and would identify those in need and let us know.

Nurse Jerith designed the CVW (Community Volunteer Workers) for LHH, following a special diploma training at Mildmay International, for community workers. This model has now been taken not only to our three hospice sites but also to other hospices within Uganda and in other African countries. Professor Barbara Jack of Edge Hill University in Liverpool has researched this work and presented it at conferences and written about it in the palliative care journals.

It is a simple plan. The team approaches the community leaders for the villages in an area and asks them to select two people who would be acceptable to the village, to help them when they are sick and also to bring them help from hospice or other organisations if they need it, and with their permission. The selected persons are trained at hospice or in the village itself, by the hospice team, in basic nursing techniques which they in turn pass on to the carers of patients in the home. They are trained to identify those in need of further care, and either bring them to hospice or meet us on an outreach to a health centre. If the patients are very sick then the team would go down to them as an emergency and advise.

Initially we found the CVWs were referring people not suitable to our programme but we then assisted them to refer these cases to the right service for them. Gradually the CVWs have become more and more skilled and are mainly referring the right patients and know enough about the other services available to refer appropriately. There were already CVWs working for the Ministry of Health in the area and some of them asked to receive the training and join our own CVWs. This has greatly assisted in our care in the District.

The original scheme was that if the CVW had proved themselves in their work after three months, they would be given a T-shirt and a bicycle, followed by 10,000 Ugandan shillings per month (£3.20 or €3.70) to maintain their bicycles. They would meet monthly with the hospice team, discuss difficult cases and have an update with teaching on a common problem they were encountering.

This scheme costs about £120 or €150 per year per CVW. It is a very cost-effective way to support those in the community. But even these small amounts have been compromised by the reduction of funds in the present recession.

For the last two years, LHH has benefited from the oil discovered in Lake Albert by Tullow Oil of Ireland. Tullow brought LHH on board, after a visit by their founder, Aidan Heavey, to Makindye in 2006. He promised to assist this work in districts which were part of the area for oil excavation. New clinics have been served by LHH down at Lake Albert, where the first oil was found. This is an area which for years was most deprived as there was no road into the area of the fishermen. A road is now there to take the car down to the lakeside. There Tullow Oil are very involved with the local community, saving the lives of the fishermen with swimming lessons and manufacturing life jackets at the lakeside, which must be worn by the fishermen. We are very grateful for their support to our patients and families.

To date, the LHH team has grown from 5 to 19, comprising management, clinical and education sections. They have increased with the site activities which presently include two site days a week, when patients attend the centre for regular appointments remembering that urgent cases are accepted at any time. There are eight outreach clinics, with home visits daily, and a weekly children's clinic. At the time of writing, in April 2010, they were looking after 364 patients. A local branch of the Palliative Care Association of Uganda brings all those working with patients together.

The CVWs now numbers 45 LHH volunteers and 70 District CVWs giving a total of 115. Jerith has now passed on the management of the CVWs and is head of the education department. She leads the training of teams in the Districts of Northern Uganda. These teams are made up of trainers from Hoima and Makindye and presently have a huge role in training support HIV teams for the north of Uganda.

'Big trees from little acorns grow!'

My daily work as a nurse at LHH
by Agaba Martin

Martin is a specialist palliative care nurse at Little Hospice Hoima.

My daily work at LHH is focused on improving palliative care patients' quality of life so that before they cross to the next world their pains are well assessed and managed holistically and they die in peace, not regretting why they were born. I make sure that such patients and their families understand that death is part of the human graph in God's creation.

As a nurse, I always do my work from Monday to Friday from 8.30 am to 5.00 pm but due to the nature of our patients we care for at long distances, in hard areas to reach and bad roads, sometimes I find myself going extra miles and end up coming back at LHH premises between 7.00 and 8.00 pm.

Early morning after prayers, I always first discuss with fellow team members about the patients cared for the previous day – how they are doing and the challenges faced. All these are discussed and the way forward is always documented in patients' files.

After discussion, I check in my home visit bag to see whether all palliative care drugs in bottles are there and refill is always done for those drugs which got finished during the last visit, and all equipment such as blood pressure machine, stethoscope, thermometer etc. are checked to make sure they are in good working condition.

Since holistic care is a key point in palliative care, I always request for comfort fund, for nutrition and basic needs from the responsible person. This is for those patients who merit assistance after assessment of their needs, and I ensure the correct documentation accompanies this, with forms which patients sign on receiving.

When everything is ready, which is always between 9.00 and 9.30 am, the driver is informed. He normally comes and assists me in lifting the bag and the other things I will be having that day. He is always briefed about the patients to be seen that day, for easy planning of the journey and directions to follow on their files.

At the patient's home

The patient and the family is the centre of palliative care. These patients are always traced using their physical (not postal) addresses and the help of community volunteer workers. Most of these patients on home visits are 30–60 km away from LHH premises and don't live near each other; it may be almost 10–15 km to reach the next patient.

Whenever I reach a patient's home, I always greet them with their carers while having a smile to create a good relationship with them. I always cherish greeting my patients with touch therapy in their hands while putting another arm on their shoulders because I have always observed that it makes many patients feel that they still have people who love them. These patients need us to be there for them because most of them, due to the disease, tend to hate themselves and feel they are no longer loved. So it's always very necessary to be there for them when they need us so that by the time God takes them, they rest in peace but not in pieces.

During my work on home visits, I always feel proud of my God because not everyone is dedicated to do such kind of work like cleaning smelly cancer wounds and touching them with one's heart. It's not easy but it's a gift from God.

Controlling physical pain using analgesic ladder depends on the patient's pain score on a numerical rating scale devised internationally. Controlling their symptoms is very important because it makes patients comfortable when they know they have a terminal illness but feel no pain and are able to sleep well.

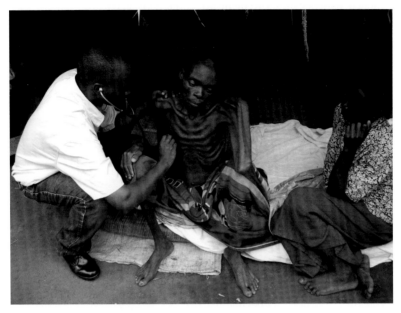

Figure 11.7 *Nurse Martin, LHH, at the patient's home.*

Whenever I am at a patient's home, I like to put quality over quantity. Proper holistic assessment is always important followed by good management. This helps to treat patients' total pain and makes them more comfortable. This is always based on the physical, psychosocial, spiritual and cultural nature of each patient.

Oral liquid morphine has been found to be a miraculous drug because it has helped to control patients' pains from 5/5 to 0/5 on the numerical rating scale (NRS). With patients' full pain control, their quality of life has been improved and their families can now rest at night, having previously been kept awake due to the patient screaming in pain, which has always made the patient and family very uncomfortable.

All patients are reviewed at home, their medications are always refilled and I always ensure that patients and their families understand the use of all drugs given and how they are supposed to be taken.

As I continue to care for these patients, I always like to put God between me and my patients. Whenever I finish giving treatment a word of prayer is always said with the patient and family. And I am not afraid to touch patients to show them affection. This leaves the patient very comfortable.

Figure 11.8 *MHM team, May 2010:* *Left to right: back row: Amina Bukenya (general assistant), Beatrice Kaganzi (nurse), John Kobweme (guard), Scholar Tugumisirize (trainer), Martha Rabwoni (health services manager), Beatrice Asiimwe (trainer), Honest Twinomuguni (nurse), George Barugahare (guard), Dr Gerald Lule (medical officer), Deborah Owokunda (general assistant); middle row: Godfrey Musitwa (accounts assistant), Betty Bifabusa (nurse), Jackson Mucunguzi (finance and administration manager; front row: Rosette Aryampa (receptionist/secretary), Helen Iyekat (trainer), Michaela Sponsheimer (volunteer social worker), John Tibayungwa (driver), Hassan Bukenya (driver).*

Figure 11.9 *Palliative care bag carried by the nurses and doctors on home visits.*

12　HAU and Palliative Care in Uganda Today

In curing the 'physician is the general',
whereas in caring 'the patient is the sovereign'.[19]

THE BEGINNINGS of Hospice Africa Uganda were very different from today. Now hospice has three sites. There are more than 1100 patients on the programmes, as shown in Table 12.1. We have looked after more than 164,000 patients since 1993. Now our education programmes take up 50% of our time and 50% of our resources. It is through those we train that we see palliative care reaching more and more in need both in Uganda and in Africa.

Table 12.1　　Patient numbers, April 2010.

Site	Patients on programme	Patients cared for to date
Makindye	448	8894
MHM	342	5186
LHH	364	1980
Total	**1154**	**16060**

Makindye is the main site of HAU in Kampala; MHM= Mobile Hospice Mbarara; LHH = Little Hospice Hoima.

The Education Department, as well as the initial courses for health professionals and volunteers, and the training of medical students which commenced in 1994, now has six core programmes for health professionals, allied health professionals (such as teachers, lawyers and other professionals), volunteers, spiritual advisors, traditional healers, and counselling for end of life care. The team also trains individual districts for the advent of oral morphine and its use, which opens the door to holistic care and support for those suffering. Hospice also trains

---

[19] Mud and Stars: a report of a working party on the impact of hospice experience on the Church's Ministry of Healing, Sobell Publications, 1991, p. 128, Ethos of cure and care.

those working in support teams to be able to deliver pain and symptom control to the very ill.

Furthermore, the teams from new hospice and palliative care services in Uganda and from other African countries are coming to HAU to see how palliative care can work in an African setting and to adapt their knowledge to their own needs.

Publications have followed these courses. Manuals to suit each training have been produced and the Blue Book, initially published for Uganda and other African countries in 1994, is now in its fourth edition and translated into French for Francophone countries in Africa.[20] The first edition of the *Clinical Guide to HIV/AIDS Palliative Care in Africa* was edited by HAU for African countries and by Dr Liz Gwyther for S Africa. Other publications are the annual reports since 1994, the quarterly newsletters and the fact sheets which are available monthly. The website gives up to date information and can be found on www.hospiceafrica.or.ug. The Irish website is equally interesting, giving the Irish approach and stressing the contribution of Ireland to the progress of Hospice Africa. This may be found at www.hospiceafrica.ie

However, as we increase our work, we increase our team. The team members now number 135 between the three sites. The figures in Tables 12.1 and 12.2 show the present achievements in patient care and training.

Table 12.2   Breakdown of individuals trained by Hospice Africa, 1993 to April 2010.

Health professionals	CVWs	DLD	CPCC	Medical students	Health tutors	Others	Total
2438	523	96	108	2358	75	1485	7083

CVWs = Community Volunteer Workers; DLD = Distance Learning Diploma; CPCC = Clinical Palliative Care Course (clinical and morphine prescribers).

---

[20] See previous footnote.

Figure 12.1 *Some of the clinical team, Makindye, Kampala, May 2010;*
Dr Jenny Ssengooba, Clinical Director (middle row, 4th from left).

Of course, as impressive as these figures are, figures and flat statistics are one thing, but the reality of working in palliative and hospice care is quite another. Therefore, to give you a sense of the reality of working in palliative care in Uganda today, I have sought the help of two nurses at Hospice Uganda whose account is the subject of the next chapter.

13 A Day in the Life of a Hospice Nurse in Kampala

by Rose Kiwanuka and Martha Rabwoni

At the heart of caring, love, hope, worth, and purpose
have to be communicated and received through language, touch and actions.
These have to be conveyed with poverty of heart and compassion.[21]

I would like to close Part II of this book with this account of the daily life of a hospice nurse, which I think vividly describes the realities of working in palliative care in Uganda today. This was compiled with the help of Rose Kiwanuka and Martha Rabwoni, my first two nurses at Hospice Africa Uganda, who have taught me so much.

*

I ARRIVE AT hospice after making sure that my children are off to school and the baby is comfortable with my baby nurse.

A distant bell rings and there is a scramble as the clinical team leave aside their computer or their talk on management of a patient to reach the Mary McAleese Lecture Theatre upstairs for the prayer and announcements which inform us all of what will be happening today at hospice. This is an important time for us. A time to commune with our God and the need for Him to accompany us as we meet new patients and care for others on the programme. We pray for those who have died and for their families as they enter this bereavement.

Then any information about today is given. Today we are expecting some visitors from Ireland and we have the medical students from Makerere in for training. They will accompany us on mobile rounds. In the group attending prayers, there are also some new *m'zungus*. These are medical students joining us for part of their electives from universities in the USA, UK and occasionally from Ireland. Sometimes the visitors on the rounds have to be curtailed for the sake of the patients who need some quiet time with the hospice team member closest to them, to be able to confide their problems and needs. Last year for the

---

[21] Mud and Stars, op. cit., p. 100.

first time, we had to refuse applications from medical students from abroad, because we had so many applications. Of course, priority must be given to the Ugandan medical students as they will carry the message forward here in Uganda.

Figure 13.1 *Mary McAleese, President of Ireland, being greeted on arrival at HAU for the opening of the Mary McAleese Lecture Theatre, 2001.*

After the announcements, the team members go back to their departments to start the day's work. I am in Team 5. We cover the area around Entebbe. Today we have four patients to see, two of whom are new to us so it will be a long day. We aim to leave by 10 am but this is often not possible with delays from meetings of groups, sorting out the nurse's bag, ensuring that all the foreseen medications have been prepared for the follow-up cases and that everything necessary for the new cases are also in the bag. These bags have a list and quantity of medications which are required before leaving on a visit as well as minimum equipment including the stethoscope, rubber gloves, catheters and dressings. Other delays surface from drivers and car problems and even delays over breakfast as we need to go out with a happy stomach as we may not get back until after 4 pm. The team leader has given the list of patients to the sister in charge the night before so the medications and case sheets are ready for us.

A relative of one of the new patients has arrived to take us to the home, which can be difficult to find on the first day. Once the driver has found the home he will not miss finding it again. This has always been amazing to our *m'zungu* friends as many homes are related to trees or other natural significant growths, such as the house third on the right from the 'big tree' ... We Ugandans are used to this way and not to following maps!

We plan to see this new patient first and then see the two follow-up cases and finally the second new case. This is all planned taking into account the site of their homes, so that we do not waste time between visits. One patient has phoned in last night as he has developed a new pain which was keeping him awake. The sister on call was able to assist him by advising on increase of his medications, but he needs follow-up this morning.

We have two medical students with us as we set off. It was raining last night so some of the *murram* roads[22] will not be easy to navigate. What's more, a couple of the homes are off the main *murram* roads and we will have to walk to reach them.

Driving in the car, we review the notes to date of each patient and the medical students ask questions and voice their concerns about handling such very ill patients at home. They have been taught that they should be in hospital. We explain that many cannot afford hospital, fear hospital because of previous bad experiences and prefer to be managed in their own homes. As they see, and get involved with each patient, these explanations become clear.

We reach the mud house where Mary lives and her relative knocks at the door.

'*Hodie!*' he cries and the response is feeble as Mary responds, '*Karibu*' (welcome).

The first patient is in a bad way. Mary was identified by the community volunteer and has never in her life seen a health worker. Now, at the age of fifty-two she has developed full-blown AIDS and the symptoms of cryptococcal meningitis. Her husband died some seven year ago. She is aware of The AIDS Support Organisation (TASO) bringing

---

[22] Tough gravel road

help to HIV positive people and was tested by them some years ago, but fearing stigma, she did not continue with TASO.

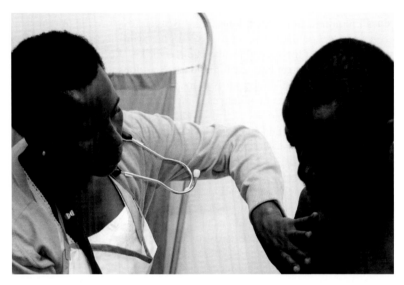

Figure 13.2 *Specialist Palliative Care Nurse Charlotte examines a patient. Photo courtesy of* The Lancet.

Later, on follow-up, she was offered antiretrovirals (ARVs), but did not go because of her fear of 'health workers'. She had a friend who was started on ARVs some years ago and she died three weeks later. It is a wonder that she allowed us to come!

Her devoted elder daughter Sarah, aged thirty-two, is caring for her. Mary has seven children from three different men, two of whom have died. She is a Catholic. The youngest child is sixteen years old and still at school. Financial support comes from the older children now earning.

The house is made of mud brick and has one room and three beds behind a curtain in the same room. The latrine is shared by three families and is about three minutes' walk from this residence. But the room is tidy. A calendar with Pope Benedict is prominent on the wall and pictures of the Virgin Mary and a crucifix indicate the adopted family religion.

However as Mary has been unable to attend church for some weeks, she is feeling guilty at not attending Sunday Mass. The priest has not been to visit her. She is afraid to tell him of her predicament because of the nature of the disease and because the children have failed to pay the 'dues' required from each household. This is due to the diminished economy, one of them having to give up her work to look after Mary, and to the cost of the special needs required for her illness.

Mary is lying on her bed in the dark. She does not like the light so we stay in the dark. Coming in from the light, we can just make out her form on the bed when she greets us. Gradually our eyes accommodate to the darkness.

Mary is wasted and in pain. Her eyes are very bright in contrast to the wasting. She is very averse to going to the hospital for a spinal tap to confirm her diagnosis. We are guests in her house so cannot enforce this. However the diagnosis is fairly certain by the signs and symptoms and confirmed by clinical examination and the signs of raised intracranial pressure. She also has a raucous cough and each time she coughs her expression is one of severe pain as the headache becomes worse.

We give her morphine early on in the history taking as she is finding it difficult to concentrate because of the pain. Much of the history is taken from Sarah, her daughter, but there are parts we need Mary to tell us. Pain is not controlled completely with the first dose of 5 mgs of morphine so we have to give a second 5 mgs thirty minutes later. Now comfortable, Mary is able to tell us her problems and we treat her symptoms and her pain, and assure her that we will be here for her and help her as long as she would like.

Physical examination makes us suspect that Mary has TB as well as meningitis. We treat her for her cough and give antifungal medicines for the suspected cryptococcal meningitis. However TB meningitis is also on the cards, except that the short onset suggests cryptococcal meningitis.

We write out her medication chart so that she will know when to take her morphine and other medications including medicine for the anticipated constipation brought on by morphine.

Her main problem at the moment is pain but we anticipate more at our next visit when she is comfortable. Once the pain is controlled she will be worrying about other problems for herself and the family. We have noted the small grandchildren peeping around the door, wondering what we are doing to JaaJaa (grandmother) and they are a source of laughter in the house and for Mary. But like all Ugandan children they are disciplined and quiet unless spoken to and encouraged to answer.

Having made Mary comfortable, we ask her if she would like us to pray with her before we leave. Her face brightens and she tells us she is happy for this. Before we pray, she tells us that she is worried that she may not make peace with God because she has not paid her dues to the Catholic Church. She is aware that she is not in good books with the priests because she married a Muslim (her last husband). Although she and the family have been practising Catholics since her husband died, she fears approaching them. We tell her that we will approach the priest on her behalf and also tell her that God loves and understands her situation and will be there for her, as Christ was there for so many women who suffered, as found in the Bible.

Her daughter joins in the prayer and at Mary's request, I lead a prayer, asking God's blessing on the family and this house as they care for Mary. We ask for healing of Mary in body and soul.

We leave Mary, with a deep feeling that we have connected, and feel suffused with her gratitude. This is what makes our work so worth while. At the next visit, when she is feeling better, we will discuss other options for her including a revisit to ARVs.

*

We follow problem-based care in hospice so the initial problem list is written at the end of the assessment forms. Mary's problems are as follows:

Meningitis – antifungal commenced
Severe headache – morphine and laxative given
Possible TB – review at next visit? for discussion with TB team
Immunosuppressed – review possible CD4 count
Religion guilt – discuss with priest with patient's permission
Financial problem – further assessment at future visit

Taking a history and attending to the needs of a new patient can take up to two hours. It is now 1 pm and we move to the follow-up patients. We are welcomed at each home. Mustafa has had deterioration and shows signs of paraplegia from extension of metastases to the spine. This is confirmed by our clinical examination of the legs which reveal weakness and changes in reflexes. He has cancer of prostate and has recently become incontinent of urine. This is an emergency. We commence him on large-dose steroids and arrange for him to be brought to the radiotherapy department the following day for emergency radiotherapy to the spinal lesion. If this is done then we can prevent the progress of the paraplegia and even bring him back to normal use of the legs.

As we approach the home of the third patient, we hear sounds of crying. A child of eight years has died this morning. Peter had Burkitt's lymphoma, which had been resistant to chemotherapy paid for by our hospice fund. He was on our children's programme and attended our day care up to two weeks ago when he was too sick to travel in the hospice car. The family tell us that he became very weak in the night and failed to waken in the morning. His parents and siblings had been prepared for Peter to go to God, but they are also devastated to lose him.

We go and see the tiny body, lying on the mat with his mother and the women sitting around him. They will keep him company tonight until the funeral tomorrow. We console them and even hug his mum, and assure her that Peter is in our prayers. We will come back and visit after the funeral. One of the Children's Team will attend the funeral if they are free.

The second new patient is our last today. Aisha is thirty-two and has cancer of the cervix and has been attending radiotherapy at Mulago. They now think that her lesion is too far advanced to assist any more. She is in severe pain. She describes it as like having a baby – only the baby does not come and the pain continues! We immediately give her 10 mgs of morphine as the pain of cancer of the cervix is one of the worst.

She also has a VVF (vesico vagina fistula) which is due to the cancer breaking through the vagina into the bladder, making a hole where the urine leaks out all day. There is no cure for this when there is cancer involved as the surgical intervention given to those with a hole due to childbirth is not possible. The cancerous tissue will not support repair. We show her our plastic panties, made by a local dressmaker and similar to Kanga pants. She will support some old cotton rags within the pants and be able to move normally, and continue her housekeeping without being afraid of the smell and constant embarrassing leaking.

She asks about her disease and her prognosis now that she is no longer attending radiotherapy. We gently bring her to the truth and ask her to call us if she has any further questions before we visit in the next few days.

Her main problem is what will happen to her four children when she dies, the eldest in P7 (seventh year of formal schooling) and the youngest at nursery. Her husband is a small-business man and the income is not regular. She also suspects he has another woman as she has not been able to give into his needs for about three months. We promise to come and talk to the husband and see if we can help. There is often an extended family that might help with intermarriage fidelity matters, but this needs to be clarified.

I feel very sad for Aisha because I too have four children and I am around her age. We all have a problem here in Uganda. Men are allowed to play away, but not women. We tell each other, 'I never know when I will be next with HIV, or even with cervical cancer.'

Again we suggest we might pray with Aisha. We pray now to God, as she is Muslim and will not be happy for us to pray to Jesus. She receives some peace from the prayer which she asks us to lead as she is so weak.

So much suffering for our women in Uganda. I feel so sad as I leave Aisha and pray that God will give her relief from her pains and peace before she dies.

We return to hospice after 5 pm. Now I need to fill in the final sheet for the statistical department before I go home. I also report to our Health Services Manager about the difficult cases and their needs.

I sit with the medical students and try to answer their questions and explain the hospice approach, which is so different to that in hospital. Our patients are our guests and have choices in how we assist them. We show them love and concern and recognise that some day we may be there in their place.

I reach home at 7 pm. My husband has fed the younger children. I am lucky in that he can assist. I have a cousin from the village who looks after the younger children while I am at work and she has managed well. But my children greet me with 'Mamma we need *you*.' I now revert to my Mamma mode!

Thank God for my family and my ability to bring some comfort to the less fortunate that I meet on a daily basis.

Tomorrow, I will be teaching in the Education Department and need to prepare for this. The children tucked up in their beds, I put on the light and start to prepare. Tomorrow early at hospice I will put my thoughts onto a slide presentation. I also need to check the emails now that I have had such a busy day.

God will be there for me.

PART III

HOSPICE AFRICA: PRINCIPLES AND PRACTICE

14   Spirituality

The spirit of Ubuntu
– that profound African sense that we are human
only through the humanity of other human beings –
is not a parochial phenomenon, but has added globally
to our common search for a better world.
Nelson Mandela[23]

When a person is dying, all life events seem to be concentrated in the short time that is left. To the Ugandan, it is also a time of renewing their relationship with God. Most of our patients like a member of the team to pray with them and answer questions eagerly about their spiritual life and their relationship with God.

We welcome those of all and any religions and encourage them in the peace of their chosen religion.[24]

MANY PEOPLE confuse spirituality with religion. It is very important that those working with people who are dying understand what spirituality is. Otherwise in a country where new religions are cropping up all of the time and converting someone new to your religion is seen as a trophy, those that are terminally ill may be used or subjected to overkill by overzealous people of one faith or another.

Spirituality is a relationship with God that often develops from childhood, regardless of whether one is or isn't a believer in God. Religion is often an introduction to spirituality and a catalyst to spiritual development. Thus, our spirituality may be linked closely with our religion, particularly in the early years of our life. However, often when faced with a crisis such as a life-limiting illness, their relationship with God becomes the most important thing for a person. This is a sudden revelation when fatal illnesses hit unexpectedly, but it is often a gradual

---

[23] Jennifer Crwys Williams (ed.), *In the Words of Nelson Mandela*, Penguin, 1997.
[24] From the HAU Annual Report 1995–96, Pastoral Care Report, p. 21.

realisation for the elderly. My experience in geriatric medicine has made me aware that as we get older, most of us seem to gradually accept that God is the most important thing in our lives.

In a recent group discussion in Ireland, a new and wider definition was accepted. Spirituality is the 'human spirit in me, relating to others and to my God or a higher being'. Spirituality and its understanding are related to the cultural and religious conditions in each country.

In order to understand our patient, we too have to experience a relationship with God. This can be very difficult if we declare that we are an atheist (i.e. we don't believe in the afterlife or in God) or agnostic (i.e. we are not sure whether God exists or not). However, all of us at some time in our lives experience something that completely lifts us out of ourselves and out of this world into something that we do not understand. This may be triggered by, for example, a beautiful sunrise or sunset, a breathtaking view, a stirring piece of music, or falling in love, and in these circumstances we experience something that makes us realise that there is something greater than I. This is a reflection of spirituality, which is part of each of us.

Spiritual stages

In order to understand ourselves and our patients better we have introduced into our discussions on spirituality at hospice the four stages of spirituality. These were described by M. Scott Peck, in his book *Further Along the Road Less Travelled.*[25] For clarity I will outline how we understand them now.

Stage 1   People of the Lie

This stage is compared to a child under the age of five who indicates a lack of understanding between a truth and a lie, between good and evil. As a child progresses through life they will change and grow, but some people are found to continue in this state throughout life. Scott Peck suggests that 60% of the people he saw as a psychiatrist were in Stage 1 and because they lied so naturally it was difficult to unravel their problems.

---

[25] M. Scott Peck, *Further Along the Road Less Travelled,* Pocket Books, 1997.

Stage 2   *Structures*

This can be compared to the child from the age of 5–12. At this time structures are the most important thing in their life. When the child is at school they live within structures and often feel lost if their structures are removed. They obey the rules. We find such people at this stage embedded in traditional religions. I can only compare it to my own religion, Catholicism: in the pre-Vatican II era we always did what we were told and never questioned anything but accepted as the 'gospel truth' all that the Church, through the priests, told us. We also see this amongst Muslims and amongst the new religions of today where absolute obedience is demanded by those in power, which is propagated by the people in Stage 2.

An example of how changing the structure can upset people was seen following Vatican II when the universal Latin Mass was changed into the common language of each country. A group of Catholics started an opposition church to hang on to the Latin Mass and other traditional formalities. These kinds of changes can really bring out the left and right wings of a religion.

Stage 3   *Searching*

Many agnostics fall into this group. The person may still be a believer but not sure of their God or of their means or way to God, i.e. which religion is going to take them to God. This can be compared to the teenager who suddenly decides they are not going to church any more with their family. The reaction of the parents is often to be extremely angry and demand the presence of the child at church which often only increases the division for the child from religion and the parents. But this step is an essential part of developing a relationship with God. This period of searching for the truth needs to be understood as part of spiritual development.

Stage 4   *Peace*

The person has now found peace within their own beliefs and life experience. This peace is usually with God and those to whom they relate. However, atheists too can find peace once they fully believe that there is no God.

Research was carried out many years ago in England to find out who was at peace at the end of their life. The result of the survey showed that those who were at peace either had great faith in their God and the afterlife, or believed that the light went out and death was the end of it. The people who were unsure were the ones not at peace. We in palliative care are trying to bring our patients to peace with God according to their beliefs and with their families. Of course, rifts within the family are often not healed in coming towards death but we can try to accompany the patients on their journey towards peace with their God.

*

At hospice, spiritual staging was a part of the general assessment for many years. Sadly this was discontinued because of the necessity to tick off boxes for donors. It is important to do but needs recurring explanations and discussions with the clinical team to keep it alive.

However staging can be applied to ourselves, especially to those of us who work in palliative care, as we should take time out to think about our own spirituality and to develop our own relationship with God, or not, and to understand spirituality. This is an interesting concept in Uganda where we have not yet met somebody who has denied the existence of God! However in the 'developed countries' there are many more these days who are not sure or who do not believe. When we have assistance from overseas personnel, we need to understand where they are coming from and ask them to understand what is acceptable in Uganda. This can be difficult.

Although spiritual staging assists our understanding of ourselves and our patients, it can also be used to research pain versus spiritual staging. We only looked at this once in a small group of people, but people who were at the stage of peace on admission to the programmes seemed to have less pain than those in the earlier stages. More research needs to be done in this area.

Africa and religion

In the countries of Africa where I have worked, religion has been a major part of life and this is not hidden from everyday life. We find, along with the favourite English League Football teams, on the *matatus* (local minibus taxis), prayers and praise of God, reflecting their trust in God to protect the driver no matter how fast he goes! Such prayers can also be found on private cars, appealing to us to be aware that 'God is the boss, God is in charge' and in Nigeria: 'God ee der.'

In Uganda, if you ask any patient their religion they will give you the local religions: Catholic, Protestant, Muslim or Born Again etc. But whatever modern religion they claim, they are also committed from birth, to the traditional religion, animism. In every village, one is expected to carry out certain rituals during one's life and often before death to the ancestors. It is very hard for Westerners to understand this but it is important that we are sensitive to it, particularly in circumstances where the patient is coming to the end of his or her life.

Ubuntu

African religious beliefs can be defined within the word 'Ubuntu'. Ubuntu is a way of life from which we in the Western countries could learn. African tradition is diverse but the philosophy of Ubuntu is a unifying factor across many African cultures.

There is no strict distinction in the African worldview between *spiritual* and *secular*. All is integrated in one vision. This integration can be used to show the vital link between the sick and the healthy; between the living and the 'living-dead' and the yet to be born. This link assures the sick of keeping his or her identity in sickness, death and after-life. The continuation of the cultural values and heritage most loved in one's life and work results in:

- Sense of real worth
- Sense of community
- Sense of God
- Sense of neatly combining the good in this-worldly life with the good-in-the-life hereafter.

These values are also found in animism in other cultures. An example would be the complete wholeness referred to in the Yin and Yang of Taoism with its relationship to the ancestors. They are also found in Celtic spirituality. John O'Donohue says: 'The Celtic imagination loved the circle. It recognised how the rhythm of experience, nature and divinity followed a circular pattern.' He calls this 'the Celtic circle of belonging'.[26]

Table 14.1   Core values of Ubuntu.

Core values of Ubuntu[27]	Associated values
Humanness	Warmth, tolerance, understanding, peace, humility
Caring	Empathy, sympathy, helpfulness, charity, friendliness
Sharing	Unconditional giving, redistribution, openhandedness
Respect	Commitment, dignity, obedience, order
Compassion	Love, cohesion, informality, forgiveness, spontaneity

Every life history is different. No one welcomes suffering but often it is that very suffering that offers us a lesson to help us in understanding each other. This suffering may be physical, or a bereavement or marriage breakdown, or any other life experience that is traumatic. As every doctor should have had an operation before qualification so as to experience what it is like to be helpless and cared for by others, palliative carers who have experienced total pain at some stage in their lives can use this experience to understand what our patients are going through and to help them.

But each individual patient has had different life experiences. Even at this point of their life, regardless of whether they are dying as children, teenagers, parents or at old age, their beliefs will be coloured by their age, marital status, professional status, culture, IQ and the social norms they were born with and how they have changed in their life. No two patients are the same and therefore we must individualise our approach to them and to their spirituality. We are trying to bring this person to peace within their own beliefs and we are certainly not there to convert them to our beliefs.

---

[26] John O'Donohue, *Anam Cara: A Book of Celtic Wisdom*, Prologue, HarperCollins, 1998.

[27] John Mary Waligo, Psychosocial and spiritual care, in: *A Clinical Guide to Supportive and Palliative Care in HIV/AIDS in Sub Saharan Africa*, APCA, 2006, p. 236.

In Africa, including Uganda, even among some of the highly educated people, illnesses are thought not to be caused by a bug or virus but by offending someone who has sought assistance through witchcraft. This somebody may be alive or dead. But until reparation is made the illness may still linger.[28] These beliefs will often affect how people access health services.

To the Buganda women, the placenta at birth is very precious and so is the cord. Both of these at childbirth need to be buried underneath a certain banana tree. If this is not done the child will have bad luck. Thus many of the Buganda women prefer to go to a traditional place for their birth, 'because you (in hospitals) throw away our placentas'. Traditional beliefs and spirituality are entwined; this makes it difficult for Westerners to understand it completely.

The health worker meeting spiritual needs

Many of our health workers feel uncomfortable with the spiritual aspect of palliative care because it is not the traditional role of the health worker to be involved in this area. But this is a very important part of holistic care and joining palliative medicine means extending our horizons.

Here we have a change from the traditional health worker. The relationship and balance between the carer and the patient needs to be adjusted in palliative care. It must be the spirituality of a companion, ready to listen without answers, of the friend that walks alongside, helping, sharing and sometimes just sitting, empty handed when one would rather run away.

So many of the existential questions we are asked if we sit and listen to patients, we are unable to answer. But they need to know they can ask us. Important points I have learned are:

- Never forget animism, a religion that forges the African spirituality.
- Rituals may need to be performed before peace can be made with God and family.

The African carer will say: 'My professed religions may have power over me. Animism also has power over me but I may not say. However I need to be able to open up. Ubuntu can guide me.'

---

[28] Ibid., part 3.

When someone is dying, if they find someone they can really trust, often the nurse, they confide in them and like to pray with them. So it has become a tradition at hospice to ask the patient before leaving the house if they would like us to pray together. This prayer can be led by the patients, the relative or the nurse. Of course it is only with experience and developing sensitivity that we learn when may, or may not be, an appropriate time to ask. For example if the patient is angry with God over their present illness, it may increase the anger and cause rejection of the team.

Praying with the patient must also be religion-sensitive. For example, we don't pray to Jesus with a Muslim or to Muhammad with a Christian.

We may lose ourselves in the praying and not open ourselves to the spiritual hurts and suffering that our patient may want to confide in us. The health worker in palliative care is often the first to discuss with the patient the possibility that death is nigh. They are usually uncomfortable discussing this with their nearest and dearest, fearful of causing them hurt and suffering. It is often healing to discuss the prognosis with the patient and the nearest relatives so that each knows what the other does and they can discuss it together.

So they may need space when the palliative care team is there to open up. We need to listen, sometimes bewildered and helpless, just sitting in silence perhaps holding hands. We need to have time in our own lives then to meditate on the many existential questions that may come to us through our patient. But sometimes it is the worries of today that come between the patient and their God. Worries like: what will happen to my children? What if another woman comes in and is cruel to them? Who will pay school fees? Why me? We must be prepared to listen and help our patients to come to terms with the unknown but above all, through us, to know a loving and caring God.

When we first come to work in palliative care and move away from curative care we often have to change our attitudes. Staff so often in hospitals appear cool, efficient, aloof and above their patients. In palliative care we develop a relationship and become a friend of our patient who is now our guest. The patient gets to make their own choices and we have to go along with these choices. Unless we have the philosophy that our patient is our guest and has choices, we will not be acceptable to them in the realm of spirituality. Unless we have this approach, we will often create a barrier which disallows any meaning in our prayer and our spiritual relationship with the person. Many of us feel uncomfortable when we first try to work with patients in this way but I assure you that this is a normal feeling as one expands one's comfort zone.

So we ourselves need to reflect on our own spirituality and the role of God in the work of palliative care. It is a privilege for the health worker, to share with this special time of life when a loved one is leaving. Looking back on the history of hospice in Uganda we can see that it was not just the people involved on this earth that moved it on but that God had a strong need for this work and is using us to bring health of spirit and peace to our patients. Every pain that is relieved and every symptom that is improved is a little resurrection for our patient. Our calling to palliative care can be called a vocation. This is more readily accepted within the clinical team that is on the first line working with patients, but when those who play a supportive role in the team have this commitment to the patient and family in their work, they are more efficient, caring and fulfilled in their work.

Bringing the importance of this concept to supportive roles at hospice such as finance and management may be more difficult. For example the committed accountant will ensure that all salaries and bills are paid on time, never leaving team members or creditors in embarrassing situations by delaying payment which is common enough in other areas in Africa! It is important that we keep this concept in everything we do. We are all here for the care of the patients and families.

At HAU, we have an annual day of reflection, which is an important support to assist the team to work holistically as a team and holistically with God.

Need for reconciliation at the end of life

Coming towards the end of life there is almost always a need for reconciliation. This is often reconciliation with loved ones, sometimes even with enemies, those we have offended and with God. This need for reconciliation is in everyone but different religions deal with it in different ways.

The Catholic Church with its concentration on guilt and forgiveness and God as a serious judge has its own ways of helping people reach peace. These ways are through the confessional and the last sacraments. Patients who are in Stage 2 of spirituality dealing with structures will accept this unquestioningly and may forget that true forgiveness comes with restitution. In Uganda we have found, particularly among the elderly clergy, that the last rites are sometimes refused to people who have not attended church regularly or who have failed to pay their dues. This refusal can cause the person on their deathbed much suffering.

In one case a lady we saw very early on in hospice life had been married in a Catholic church. Her husband began abusing her and she left him after a couple of years. She then met another man of a different faith whom she married; he gave her eight children and looked after her with great care. As she was dying at the age of forty-eight, this man showed incredible compassion and love, being with her night and day in the hospital to assure her comfort and care.

She asked the palliative care team to assist her to make reconciliation with the Catholic Church so we brought the hospital chaplain to her. However, after talking with her, he refused to give her the last rites unless she divorced the man she was currently with and who was taking such care of her. She was ready to do this with much trauma to her husband and the children. So what did the palliative care team do? We found a sympathetic *m'zungu* priest who thought on the same lines as ourselves. What would Christ have done if he was on earth for this woman? He gave her the last rites and she died peacefully, united with God and her husband at her side, a week later.

So spirituality means getting to know our God, not always as he was in the Old or New Testament, but as he would be in today's world. Christ has a heart but he works through our hearts and it is our relationship with God that allows us to support patients by knowing and remembering that this is a forgiving God.

A book that is very comforting to carers and to patients alike is *Life After Life*[29] by Raymond Moody. This book was written while Moody was a psychologist, when he carried out a study on people who had had near death experiences. The classical example of his study is of the person who has a heart attack, appears to be dead, is resuscitated and brought back to life. But this also occurs in road traffic accidents and other serious accidents in which the person nearly dies and yet survives.

Moody studied these experiences across cultures and religions and found that there was frequently a common trend in their stories: at first people have the sensation of being outside their bodies, often at ceiling level of the room. They watch what is going on and hear everything that

---

[29] Raymond A. Moody, *Life After Life*, Rider, 2001; www.lifeafterlife.com

is being said. Then they feel that they are being drawn into a tunnel and at the end of this tunnel is a comforting light.

As they travel though this tunnel they see their lives passing before their eyes. When they come to a life experience in which they know they have done wrong the 'comforter' showers them with unconditional love and tells them that these were learning experiences to bring them closer to God. This comforting light is all embracing and most people feel they do not want to return to their bodies away from this presence. But many are aware that someone who loves them dearly is crying and begging them to come back. After they have recovered, many of these people have lived changed lives, realising that all that matters in life is love for each other. This modern research only emphasises a loving and forgiving God.

Spiritual care in children

Every child is different and every age in childhood is different. In early childhood we find that the child trusts very easily, believes without questioning and gives love unconditionally. The older and more mature child will go through the stages of grief. So when we see a child we must remember to try to understand their level of comprehension. We must also understand that children are very vulnerable to guilt and often blame themselves for their own sickness and for the illnesses in other members of the family. Often they will keep asking the same questions which will give clues and insights to their troubles. Troubles for them are intensified when, as having been accustomed to being with their own peer groups, in sickness they are removed from these groups and are often placed with adults who may not know or understand them.

So what can we as hospice people do? We need to spend time with this child. We can ask them questions like: do they pray, how do they pray and how do they see God? This will take time. We must prepare ourselves to love a child and be loved by the child. Loving a child unconditionally often means that we may suffer later on, but we must not be afraid to love them because the joy often exceeds the pain.

How do I introduce spirituality to a child? Keeping in mind the age and level of understanding of the child, ask the child about her perception of God. Does she see God as a loving father or a strict, punishing father? Is she afraid of God? Explain that God loves her and is not going to punish her. Explain that God's love is with her and will continue to be with her. I too will be here for her.

We as carers can become a reflection of God's love to a child, if we are not afraid to share without imposing our own beliefs.

Figure 14.1 *Dr Liz Namukwaya and PC Nurse Octivia Naziwa with Sarah, 2007, who taught us so much about a child's spirituality.*

Ask the child to pray. Listen as the child prays. We can learn a lot from a child's prayer. What are her favourite prayers? Does she ever talk to God as a friend, tell God her worries, get angry with God, share the good things in life and thank God? These are only clues because every child is different as we are all different. But it is a great blessing to be able to see and share in the simplicity of a child's spirituality.

My spirituality: centring prayer[30]

In May 2007 we had the privilege of a visit by Bishop Kevin Dowling from South Africa. Kevin is a deeply spiritual person who spends a lot of his time with the abandoned, suffering and dying in a township in South Africa. He placed the hospice ethos at the core of the talk that he gave at hospice. I will be discussing the hospice ethos in the next chapter, but he

---

[30] Much of this section is from all we learnt from Bishop Kevin Dowling of South Africa, from his talks to patients, carers and teams in May 2007, as our Guest for the Palliative Care Week in Kampala.

stated categorically that we the carers need spirituality if we are to be a caring team and if caring is truly to overflow to those for whom we care. Spirituality opens the door to God being present though us and acting through us. He stated that through hospice caring we are united. We are called by God and this is a vocation. But having been called by God we can expect that God will gift us with all that we need for our ministry to the sick. We can trust God to be with us every day and in every moment.

This invites us into a relationship with God every moment so that we can open a door to God being present in us and acting through us for our patients. The fruit of this will be God's work continuing through our work. So how do we develop our relationship with our God? It is important to take time out and reflect on what God wants to do with us and in us each day. God is moulding us into 'our dream' through everything that happens every day. There is nothing that cannot be taken and used by God in his daily moulding of us. Even our failures can be remoulded to bring good to others.

We need to be in the presence of God and to be aware that God can be present in us. This is the God who knows and protects me, as explained in Isaiah 43:1–3 (the Old Testament is used a lot by Muslims and these words are relevant to us all):

> Do not be afraid for I have redeemed you. I have called you [*vocation*] by your name . . . you are mine . . . should you pass through waters I will be with you . . . or through rivers, they will not swallow you up . . . should you walk through fire you will not suffer . . . the flame will not burn you [*but don't try that yourself*] since I regard you as precious you are honoured and I love you.

Another text from Isaiah 49: 3, 4, 6:

> God said, 'You are my servant through whom I will show myself.' [*that's us!*] But I said, 'My toil has been futile I have exhausted myself for nothing and no purpose yet all the while my cause was with God.' [*How often do we people working in hospice feel like this?*] but God said to Isaiah, 'It is not enough for you to be my servant. I shall make you a light to the peoples . . . so that my salvation may reach the most remote part of the earth.' [*We are only pushing for Uganda and the rest of Africa so what a job for Isaiah!*]

This text gives insight into God's call to us in hospice. Isaiah 42:1-4, 6-7:

God says, 'Here is my servant that I care for ... my chosen one in whom my soul delights . . .
He/she does not break the crushed reed ... nor quench the flickering flame ...'
[*We need to be sensitive to the vulnerability of our patients and our team members*]
'I have taken you by the hand and moulded you . . . I have made you a covenant to the people and light to the nations . . .
To open the eyes of the blind, to free captives from prison, and those who live in darkness from the dungeon.' [*The marginalised are in special need of palliative care.*]

God might speak to a nurse in hospice and say, 'You have taken away the smell, you have taken away the pain and thus every resurrection brings light to those you care for. You have shared your spiritual self with this person.'

Our call in hospice is to a spirituality of presence. The ethos expresses the spirit of the way we relate and work with our people, the sick and the dying. Our ethos needs to be based on spirituality that we can live out in any moment of the day. This need not be complicated and does not require special, ideal circumstances: any quiet place without interruptions can be used. It is essentially simple, a spirituality of being present to myself and to the God within me. This is what we call 'centring' prayer.

It requires a bit of practice but in doing so it can almost become a habit. When you are alone for even two or three minutes, just relax, quieten the mind and be aware of the rhythm of the breathing, then centre yourself on the still point within you. Be aware that God is within that still point. You might find it useful to use a mantra with your breathing, for example:

Loving God (*breathing in*) . . . I trust in you (*breathing out*) . . . oh God of peace (*breathing in*) . . . please heal my sick (*breathing out*).

We can practise this kind of prayer at any moment of the day. As we go on home visits and come to the door of the home for a few brief seconds, be present with yourself, be present to God within your still point, then breathe a short mantra,

Lord speak through me to my sick (*in*) . . .. Lord please help me during this visit (*out*) . . . Lord help me to bring your peace to my patient . . .

We can make it very personal, for God is using us and each of our personalities to give his love to these people.

Team spirituality

Team gathering and meetings are very important. This allows us to be present to each other and present to God who is within each one of us. This creates an atmosphere of caring and loving support so that we can create a safe place for each other to share whatever is within us. This too can be enhanced and blessed through prayer. We can consciously bring God into meetings.

In Hospice Uganda, these times together have been very important. Right from the beginning we would say morning prayers with the team, which was at first small and is now much larger. We are together to share in prayer what has happened and what might happen today. Prayers are said at the start of our board and management meetings and all other meetings addressing the needs of the patients and families. Our Annual Day of Reflection is most important to us as a team as well as for individuals. This time of prayer and reflection unites us again for a new year of care for our patients and families. It also gives us an increased awareness of our responsibilities to support each other.

Hospice care and service is a ministry of God. From time to time we need to remind ourselves of the spiritual values contained in our ethos and spirit. We need time to be really healed by each other as we face difficult issues and problems or when we are tired and worn out by stress and personal pain. We need to listen to each other so we can notice the signs when someone else is down. We need to respond immediately with care, for this spirit of caring for each other will then overflow into all we do for our sick and dying. If we practise our listening, caring, loving, compassion with each other, this is what we in turn bring to the sick and dying and their families. Spirituality is for every moment of our life and work. It should also be continued when we go home to our families and loved ones because we are the same people all of the time.

We need guidance during our lives and so do our patients. Father Joseph Achetti, Camboni Father, gave us invaluable guidance in the early days (and later built Reach Out Mbuya); we are now receiving care at days of reflection from Father Brendan Jordan, MHM. Now back in Italy after nearly 50 years in Uganda, Fr Joseph continues to pray for our work and our patients. The Achetti meetings, where we share spiritual aspects of our work with the PCAU organisations, happen every quarter and are alive and well!

Our unique presence

We make God present though the kind of person we are. We are all unique and very special. The way we listen, the way we speak, the way we look at another person, the way we bring God to them is unique. No one else can do this in my way and no one else can do this in your way. I have a special way of bringing God's presence to my sick, dying and the families and my team. That is why my personal spirituality and being present to the God in me is so important. In addition, we can be aware of the presence of God in others for we are all blessed by God with different talents and gifts. This does not make me better than you, it simply means that we are all different and all of the different gifts and talents combined and used together will greatly bless and enrich our team. All of these gifts are used by God in our work with our sick and dying.

God and our sick and dying

 Sickness and dying are very unique and special times in a person's journey through life. In addition to the way we provide nursing care, our specialty in hospice is to provide care for the whole person. This includes the control of pain and symptoms, provisions of psychosocial support and spiritual care adapted to the cultural beliefs. We can only be spiritual carers if we are spiritual people having a loving relationship with God or a supreme being, in all the moments of the day. Listening to God, we can speak God's words, pray freely with the people and reassure them with conviction that God is a God of love and compassion.

Many of the sick and dying are filled with worries from the past, troubles and difficulties in the present (family, children), and fears about the future. Above all, they need a spiritual healing that can only come from God. This healing can come from God through us by the way we listen, speak and pray with our patient. We can even use the word of God (Holy Bible or the sacred texts of other religions) in a way that enables them to feel that God is actually speaking to them personally.

Just in passing, there may be significant problems for us in the different beliefs and approach of charismatic Pentecostal groups who try to persuade people not to take our medicine and to believe that God will heal them of AIDS and cancer through their prayer services. This will destroy peace of mind for the patient. We try to explain to the patient that God would expect them to take all the help available today. Not only what was available in the past, but in present times. However, the patient's choice has to be respected and sometimes we cannot persuade them; thus we can only assure them that we will never abandon them and are always here for them.

We can open the way for people to meet God by our peaceful respect, acceptance, and reverence for the person *as they are*. By our compassion, understanding and love, we reveal to them, just by being present with them, that God is present to them even though they may not believe or don't want to believe. In God's own time they often come to a moment of peace and our presence may have helped open the doors to that moment. Even if they don't find peace before death we simply entrust this person to our loving God. God understands and knows so much more than we can ever know or understand. We must simply be present in love with our patient and place everything in God's hands.

Those who don't believe

Sometimes we meet someone who says they do not believe in God at all or they do not want anyone to pray with them because they are very angry at God: 'How can God be a God of love when I am so sick?'

We must not be surprised at all by this nor try to show any surprise. We must respond calmly and with peace, accepting the person as they are, staying with them and reassuring them that we will be there for them as long as they want. We don't need to talk about God if they don't believe and or do not want to. This is important. We simply talk and share about what is important to them, uncovering values and goodness in them as their lives and their stories unfold.

The sixth stage of grief

The five stages of grief are described well. These are in fact manmade structures that we can hang our hats on and we are trying to bring our patients to the final stage of peace. The bringer of palliative care must understand these five stages as they help us to understand what it is our patient is going through. These are:

1.   disbelief, denial
2.   anger

3.   bargaining
4.   depression
5.   acceptance and peace

Nearly everyone undergoing a long and drawn out illness will wonder why God does not take them. Many elderly in our own culture go through this, especially if they have seen their offspring go to God before them. We have called this the *sixth* stage of grief.

These thoughts are particularly vivid when scarce resources in the family for food or school fees are being used for the sick person. And so if we are close to our patients, we may be asked to help them to die quickly to relieve the suffering on the family or improve the scarce resources. We must not be shocked at this. We need to explain to the person that this is a normal reaction. But we cannot help them to shorten their life. They are loved by their family and every day is precious at this time. We will be there to share their fears and worries and be there with them as needed.

God's plan for us

Again we refer to Jeremiah 29:11–14,

> 'I know what plans I have in mind for you.' God declares. 'These are plans for peace and not for disaster . . . to give you a future and a hope . . . when you call to me and come to pray to me I shall listen to you . . . when you search for me you will find me . . . when you search whole heartedly for me I will let you find me.'

In conclusion, our spirituality will include the mystery of dying and rising and understanding of the relationship between life and death. Holistic palliative care must include quality service and care for the whole person, including the spiritual dimension:

> How can I understand a figure or statistic unless I have held the hand it represents? The people we are talking about are the same as us. By the way we treat them we know just how much like Jesus we have become.[31]

---

[31] Dr J. P. Muliyil, epidemiologist with Chad, ECC, Velore, India, quoted in Gillian Paterson, *Love in a Time of AIDS: Women, Health and the Challenge of HIV-+72*, World Council of Churches, 1996.

15 Development of the Hospice Ethos

It is important not to let the authoritarian approach appropriate in acute medical emergencies and surgical emergencies to take over in other situations.[32]

A S I WRITE this chapter I am very aware, that I do not always practise what I preach. But I still try to move forward and I constantly have to remind myself that I am very human and prone to fall. And so, to quote from the old adage, while asking for God's forgiveness, 'Do what I say, not what I do.'

Developing the ethos and maintaining the spirit

What is an ethos? The definition of ethos, in the Oxford English Dictionary, is '*the characteristic spirit*, prevalent tone of sentiment, of a people or community; the "genus" of an institution or system.' One must portray the type of traits most valued within a society (hospice). Ethos is related to 'ethics' and is a guide to integrity.

Why does hospice and palliative care need an ethos? If we cannot work well with each other we cannot work with the patients and families. End of life is a special time for everyone involved. We are privileged to walk beside our patients and their loved ones. This spirit of sharing and generosity which comes from our hospitality must survive if this care is to go to all in need. It will survive if we have internalised our ethos individually and as a team.

Hospice team members need to portray the traits most valued in the hospice ethos. I have already described the struggle I had with trying to have this ethos instilled into the Nairobi hospice. The main thrust of the ethos as I understand it is:

---

[32] Mud and Stars, op. cit., p. 128.

> **1.   The patient and families are the centre of care**

But on reflection it is obvious that unless we care and respect each other we cannot give all that is needed to patients and families during this special time of life.

> **2.   We will respect and care for each other**

The above two aspects of the ethos are the most important but there is one more aspect.

> **3.   We will respect and share with our networking organisations**

Patient and family

The patient and family are our guests and will have choices in their relationships with us, their treatments, and what secrets they want to share. And they are reassured that we will not abandon them whatever their choices.

This ethos also encompasses the unpopular patient. Some patients can be very difficult, especially during the course of a long illness. Strangely enough this is more common in health professions and people who have had a greater standing in life, e.g. politicians and teachers. It is less often seen when dealing with village people except with the local community (LC) chairmen.

Figure 15.1 *The patient and family are the centre of our care.*
Octivia Naziwa (left) with patient and family, 2007.

This difficulty in accepting that life must end arises from the inability to have reflected that life is short, that we cannot always be in charge, and that we have to be humble enough to let other people care for us when our time comes. It behoves all hospice team members to take this seriously to heart and to reflect on our own deaths. This will make us better team members working at this special time of life.

The five stages of grief were given in the previous chapter, but to recap they are: (1) disbelief, denial; (2) anger; (3) bargaining; (4) depression; (5) acceptance and peace.

Patients and relatives go through these five stages but they might not go through them at the same time or in parallel. Thus we may find a patient who is relatively calm and a family who is angry. The palliative care team has to be able to deal with any eventuality calmly and without taking it personally.

Recently we came across a situation in another country. A patient who had actually been a nurse at hospice had left after having disagreements with the person in charge. When he developed cancer within a few months of leaving hospice, the family was convinced the hospice had put a spell on him. Sadly, the reaction of the hospice itself was to be angry and deny care to this family. It was only when a palliative care nurse from another country took it up that reconciliation became possible.

This could have been avoided if the hospice ethos had been accepted within this team. Thus we need to be very careful that anyone coming to hospice for the first time must accept our ethos wholeheartedly, so they can make appropriate actions and decisions.

How does an ethos affect me and my patient? My mood is reflected to my patient. If I have conflict at work or even at home and carry it with me, I cannot reflect caring and peace to my patient. I need to cast my cares aside and approach the patient with a generous heart. If I feel that I own palliative care I will be in conflict with other people and organisations. I need to respect and uphold our own teams and those of the networking organisation.

'All you need is love' – to quote from the Beatles.

The development of the present hospice ethos arose possibly from the negative impact that was seen from some hospices throughout the world. These are such things as major disagreements in philosophy and principles, and fighting that only mine is right. This can destroy the spirit of love between hospices and within a hospice. I saw this in my early days in the English hospices within the teams and with networking organisations. I found in the UK that it was often connected with fundraising, meaning every hospice was dependent on raising funds for their own work so if another began to tread on their territories for fundraising, great rivalry occurred causing conflict. Money is truly the root of all evil.

These problems both internal and external can become quite nasty. Of course nobody is perfect and no organisation is perfect. But organisations are usually created to help people who are suffering in this world by people who have the best of intentions. The founders have tried to extend this initial vision and passion into the teams. A spirit gradually forms over the years giving rise, from time to time, to comments such as

'This is not the spirit of hospice.' This comment reflects the fact that the speaker is part of an organisation that has taken ownership of the ethos or 'spirit'. This spirit gradually grows with a new organisation and it is only later that it can be more clearly defined and even changed or added to as the organisation develops.

In the year 2000 I wrote an Ethos for Hospice Africa Uganda. We talked about it and discussed it in hospice for a short period of time but it was soon overtaken by everyday work. However, in 2004 when Dr Ekie Kikule was trying to work with external consultants on the five-year strategic plan, a consultant asked her if hospice had an ethos. When she replied yes, the consultant was very surprised, since few organisations actually had an ethos that is written down.

So, again, it was resurrected and printed in 2007. It is not only for Hospice Africa but is written to assist the hospices we are supporting and others in Africa. It is now available as the 'Ethos and Spirit of Hospices in Africa' on our website and is reproduced at the end of this book as Appendix C.

In working with new initiatives throughout Africa, we have noted that progress often come to a standstill due to the power of one person with a bureaucratic approach. Bureaucracy is anathema in a hospice, as I have stated earlier, but is ubiquitous in Africa. This makes it difficult to be accepted by those within government, or who have inherited and internalised the previous bureaucratic structures of a colonial power.

Having looked at the hospice ethos in principle, what is it in practice?

The ethos in practice

It is very difficult to adhere to such an ethos on a daily basis. It is even more difficult to ensure that it is internalised in a team that is growing rapidly. Unless new employees are mentored and given the opportunity to learn about the history and ethos of hospice, they will come into this work as if it were any other job on a production line, coming in the morning and going home in the evening and collecting a salary once a month. But hospice is more than this.

In a culture where children are brought up at their mother's knee being taught that their family, and at most their neighbours in the community, are the most precious in the world, it is difficult to change to a philosophy that cares for everybody, reaching out to those of whatever tribe, whatever religion, whatever life history even if it includes rape, stealing or murder. These people when they are suffering need care. Indeed it is a human right to have such care.

Yet, we need self-sacrificing people to carry this through to all in Africa today. Any hospice that is based on lining the back pocket of the founder(s) and their families will not survive. But not only this, it will give a very bad impression of hospice and the ethos of hospitality for all. The two prongs of the hospice ethos as mentioned above are the patient and family as the centre of care and secondly that the hospice team must care for each other.

This ethos should be absorbed into networking organisations such as palliative care organisations and even continental organisations like the African Palliative Care Association (APCA). It may sound as though we in Hospice Africa have it right, but one of the things in the ethos is that we must be humble enough to admit when we are going wrong and come back to it to try to heal differences within the team and networking organisations and continue to grow.

It can be seen from the above that if the ethos is to continue, people who take responsibility for the hospice should understand the ethos fully. In this way they can provide positive guidance and help to ensure the fulfilment of the hospice mission, putting the patient and family at the centre of all they do.

Is palliative care then a vocation?

Working with the critically ill and the dying is a special calling and it is usually a joy. The reason I say this is because of the closeness we gain between ourselves and our patients. Also, because of the modern methods of palliative care and the fact that we have affordable medications that work in the African situation, we see our patients relieved of their pain and symptoms within their own homes, where they want to be, which brings joy to the patient as well as the family.

We are now in a very privileged position, as patients share their joys and hopes with us and often become our special friends. Occasionally at the death of one of our patients, a team member may become very upset because of the relationship they have formed with the deceased. But the fact that we have been well prepared, knowing that our patient friend has only a short time on this earth, means we are better prepared than the family for such a loss.

In talking about this I must refer to Dame Cicely Saunders. On two occasions before she married, she had fallen in love with patients. The first was the Polish refugee I have mentioned before, David Tasma, whom she met in 1948 in a hospital ward. David was an agnostic Jew and Cicely was a keen Evangelical Christian, but this did not make any difference to their affection for each other.

As I discussed earlier, David Tasma is famous today for his window at St Christopher's which was paid for with £500 left to Dame Cicely in his will. Again, here are his beautiful is words to her, which resonate throughout the world: 'I only want what is in your mind and in your heart.' Every dying patient who gets close to us is asking this of us.

Cicely fell in love for the second time with a Polish man called Antoni. This was while she was working at St Joseph's Hospice in London, researching pain and symptom control which was to be the hallmark of palliative care throughout the world. St Christopher's was yet to be opened in 1967. Cicely had a kindred spirit with the Polish, perhaps because of their huge suffering as a nation, and later married Marian, a Polish artist.

Antoni was a very spiritual person and a dedicated Catholic. And then one day when Cicely went to Antoni with the results of his tests, his daughter Anna said to Cicely, 'My father has so much fallen in love with you, doctor.'

For Cicely, her world suddenly became unmade without warning. She described this as 'the hardest, the most peaceful, the most inhibited and most liberating experience I have ever had'.[33] In describing her intimate feelings when in love, Cicely has given us permission to feel and love our patients without regrets or nervous breakdowns!

Cicely's bereavement after Antoni died is well described in Shirley du Bulay's biography. It was a very traumatic time for her. But don't we all fall in love with our patients – just a wee bit?

> Through the last experience with Antoni, she felt she had a glimpse of love in eternity in one golden moment of unity with our Lord. She learned that it was possible to live a lifetime within a few weeks. That time is a matter of depth and not length. That in the right atmosphere and with pain controlled so that the patient is free to be himself, the

---

[33] Boulay and Rankin (2007), op. cit., p. 108.

last days can be the richest. That they can be a time of reconciliation, that makes the dying peaceful and the mourning bearable.[34]

In caring for people the giving is a two-way street and the caring is mutual. The patient gives to the carer as much as the carer gives to the patient.

I have seen my Ugandan nurses cry when they are at a patient's funeral or when they have heard bad news. I think this is a beautiful thing because it confirms that we really care and are human. In allowing ourselves to cry, it also allows others to cry as well.

We in hospice need to be spiritual persons – and please note that, as I said in the previous chapter on spirituality, this does not mean religious. It means that we need a relationship with self and God where we can talk with him, get angry with him and pray for our patients on every occasion with him. When they need our help, and we feel we have nothing else to offer, we can plead with him, 'Oh God I am helpless. Please help my patient.'

We must also be ethically correct and be people of integrity. This means that we must never lie to a patient but gently guide them to the truth. I will never refuse to care for a patient in need, for any reason.

Developing the heart, the integrity and professionalism, requires a vocation. And it should be noted that in Uganda, as well as in other countries in Africa and elsewhere, *if we are stressed by this kind of work itself, it is probably not our vocation.*[35]

The independent hospice versus the hospital-centred hospice

In spite of the struggles, hospice has learned the hard way how difficult it is to commence a programme from grass roots level, which is the way most new initiatives are starting. We also learned that free-standing hospices are essential to bring in the ethos and spirit of hospitality so essential to palliative care.

---

[34] Boulay and Rankin (2007), op. cit., p. 86.

[35] Stress is common within hospices due to human interactions and our human failings with each other. This is different to stress from our interaction with patients and families.

Hospitals throughout the world tend to be bureaucratic, although this is improving in the West. However in Africa, as I have stated before, bureaucracy is alive and well and there is a great need for a free-standing hospice with the ethos of a sharing community to set the standards. This is particularly essential within the present African health systems.

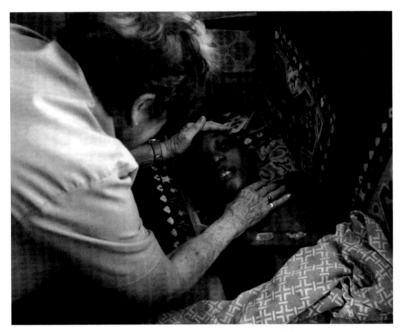

Figure 15.2 *Anne with a patient (Noel) at home, 2008.*

16 Moving and Shaking in Hospice Africa and Beyond

The community needs the dying to make it think of eternal issues and to make it listen and give to others.
Cicely Saunders[36]

HOSPICE AFRICA never conceived that we would be the only service assisting our patients and families. If that had been our role, we would have failed miserably. Rather, we see that with a 'model' which is used for training others, it is through those we have trained that this form of care will move to more and more in need. However, after seventeen years we are nowhere near the task of bringing peace before death to all those suffering from cancer, AIDS and other diseases. It is slow but it is moving. We must also work with the networking organisations, sharing with them, learning from them better ways to reach the poor in the villages wherever we go.

But from the above, it can be seen that education programmes are a most important part of our work and this education must be based on an excellent clinical service. Yet between these two services on the ground, there is the public health approach. This incorporates policies founded on good clinical research. It is based on the needs of the country, on checking out the epidemiology of the country and the real health needs at any one place at any one time. This has to be done with the awareness that the country situation, the economics, the wars, the patterns of sickness and death, the health workers available, will all have an impact on the services that can be provided.

Palliative care in Africa needs a fund of health workers not only trained, but willing to give a good service to those in need. The heart of palliative care, where the patient and family are the centre and their needs are paramount, can change the face of medicine in Africa. Many health workers have given up on the humanitarian approach because they have seen so much suffering that they are unable to do anything about. But they need to be uplifted with the hope that palliative care can bring,

---

[36] Shirley du Boulay and Marianne Rankin, *Cicely Saunders, the Founder of the Modern Hospice Movement*, p. 109.

when in the hands of a caring team. There is never a situation where we cannot do something to improve matters for the patient. We must never say again, 'There is nothing more we can do.'

So, all of our training programmes have a session on the hospice philosophy at the beginning, to set the scene. Seeing the suffering of our patients in Africa has been heartrending. How will I ever get to Heaven, I think, when these lovely people, this lovely person, has had so much suffering in such a short life?

God, where are you? is a constant cry from the palliative care team, and we need to have a deep faith to realise that we can do something about it. But also a deep realisation that we must be prepared to be a conduit for God's compassion by using our whole self, heart, soul and mind to help our patient. We need to learn, appreciate and bring the modern methods of care derived from the care and research of Dame Cicely to our people in Africa today. A formidable responsibility ...

Our moving and shaking therefore starts with our patient. Then moves into our training areas where every trainer has to have this special heart for the work and is also able to use the methods of adult education, appreciating the talents of those we teach, encouraging them gently with respect, so that those who are learning see the heart for the patient and family, transmitted through each trainer and teacher.

One of the movers and shakers who joined us in 1996 and was with us on and off up to 2007 when she joined the Infectious Disease Institute (IDI) as head of education, was Lydia Mpanga. I considered Lydia as the person who would carry on the baton, as did Cynthia Goh in Singapore. Indeed they have a lot in common. Lydia spent her very early years in London where she was in exile with her family. After coming back to Uganda for some years she returned to Oxford to read Medicine and to complete her postgraduate studies. Part of her postgraduate work had been in Sunderland where she met with Rose Kiwanuka, who was based for a short time at the hospice where Lydia was a doctor. I met her by chance in the corridors of Mulago where it was moving to see patients dressed in the Hospice Uganda T-shirt. Lydia immediately pounced on me to ask about Rose and about HAU. She joined us then as a volunteer and later came on board as the clinical consultant and later as the leader of education.

Lydia is multitalented. If you hear her on the phone you think you are speaking to the Queen of England! If you hear her singing you are transported to Heaven! She used her many talents to bring joy to the patients and to the team. Her education and clinical skills moved forward the education department. We were so sad to lose her. But she still leads palliative care in IDI and refers those interested to us for further training or support. She had a romantic courtship and wedding and now is the mother of three lovely children. Dr (Mrs) Lydia Mpanga Sebuyira is still part of us at HAU.

Figure 16.1 *Dr Lydia Mpanga Sebuyira (right) visiting hospice at a PCAU update, 2008.*

In each country we support, we use the public health approach, looking at the wider picture in the country in which palliative care must fit. Using governments, we bring in the medications required for the patients. The morphine journey was difficult in Uganda but it has worked. This is now moving to other countries. We need to work with our governments so that this care can reach anyone who accesses a health service, through health workers trained from palliative care centres.

Throughout the seventeen years of HAU, there has been a progressive move forward to help patients access the service. This involved increasing the prescribers with the change in the Government statute (2002), increasing the training for Africa with the introduction of the Distance Learning Diploma (2004) and this year (2010) bringing it to degree level. It also involved joining with Makerere University to set up a palliative care unit under the Department of Medicine (2008), based on the teaching provided from HAU since 1993.

HAU Special Children's Programme, 2007

Pictures speak louder than words here. Started by Dr Justin Amery, a consultant from Oxford who came for a year, this has moved forward so that there is a special children's programme at each hospice. The training programme that commenced in hospice has been taken throughout Africa and we are delighted at this. It is making a difference.

Figure 16.2 *(above) Children in the Cancer Institute, mainly suffering from Burkitt's lymphoma enjoy pictures and fun; (right) James with a huge tumour is able to smile because the pain is well managed. Photo of James courtesy of Abby Probasco.*

Makerere University and the New Palliative Care Unit, 2008

This was set up after several years meeting with the key people, the Deans and Head of Medicine at Makerere University.

From the beginning we had a relationship with key members in the university. Professor Ignatius Kakande brought us in and we have provided a service to patients three times a week and training to medical students since 1993. Dr Elly Katabira was one of the first to come and teach on our training programmes for health professionals. We have learned so much from him. He is a high flyer in the world of medicine who is as close to what is going on at village level as he is to the recent advances in HIV and treatments. Originally a neurologist, he came in to support patients with HIV/AIDs in 1988 and through his clinics at Mulago and in TASO has probably more experience than anyone in their care. He was the Dean when we started negotiating for the new Unit of Palliative Care. Professor Harriet Mayanja was the Head of Medicine and she was really enthusiastic.

Figure 16.3 *Dr Mhoira Leng and her palliative care team in Mulago Hospital, 2009.*

After two years of meetings we were able to appoint Dr Mhoira Leng, with experience in the University of Aberdeen and palliative care in several developing countries. She luckily came with her own funding from the organisation she had founded, Cairdas in Scotland, with a mission to spread education in palliative care in the world. This department is moving forward with teaching in the university and working with HAU we are learning from each other. Her first lecturer is home grown and trained at HAU, Dr Liz Namukwaya.

They have a university brief for education, research and clinical provision of care. A brief that is very much shared with the tertiary

Institute of Learning (2010) at HAU where the diploma and degree in palliative care for Africa and affiliated to Makerere University are taught.

Meanwhile the core short course training programmes carried out since 1993 continue. These are for health professionals already in practice, allied professionals including teachers, lawyers and others who carry forward advocacy to the communities, community volunteers and other carers, traditional healers and spiritual leaders.

The longer courses include:

- training of tutors for the nursing and clinical officer schools which are for nine weeks, including clinical components;
- Course in Palliative Clinical Care (CPCC) which provides nurses and clinical officers with the clinical skills of examination, diagnosis and treatment of those in need of palliative care and also the public health approach to providing a service in a district; this also equips them to prescribe morphine for the patient and they are registered with the Ministry of Health as prescribers;
- Distance Learning Diploma and Degree in conjunction with Makerere University, and APCA.

Over the years, numerous manuals have been produced to accompany each of the courses. The Blue Book continues to be the bible for the case that accompanies the health worker into any situation where there is a need of our care. Health workers are encouraged to consult this book for any problems that might arise. The Resource Centre and the internet give access to other books and journals at local and international levels to support the trainees and those of us who need to know more to keep up with advances in the field.

So what have been the challenges?

1. We were founded for cancer patients. This condition is growing but the funding is not yet in place for the relief of their suffering in Africa; while in the West millions are going into a search for a cure, in Africa people waste away and die in pain, when we have known how to control this suffering, in an affordable way, since 1967.
2. We were founded for cancer, but working with oncologists has been a problem all over the world. We need a better relationship and understanding of each other, working in harmony so that the patient is the focus of all that we do together, and that rivalry is removed. Working with AORTIC (African Organisations for Research and

Training in Cancer) has been a blessing and is moving forward on oncology and palliative care.

3. We need to put more time into the organisational structures and Boards of Governance, ensuring that members are chosen for their understanding of the ethical values of palliative care and mentored gently and carefully for some months after joining the Board.

4. I am worried about the continuation of the work when I am gone. One of the things I and the other founders have done is to bring trust to the donors who have been with us from the start. We have met them halfway personally, through emails, through phone calls. Thus we have had good relationships with our donors. But as we grow bigger and people join us without the knowledge of the initial struggles, then they do not have the same personal approach to donors. We must try and capture this and maintain it. We must pass on the baton with love.

5. I am convinced that the ethos and spirit of palliative care in Africa is essential for our patients to receive the caring they deserve. I pray that no board or other individual will ever be given the power to change this.

Figure 16.4   *Dr Robert Twycross, whom I have always considered 'the first son' of Dame Cicely Saunders. His research, training and publications have taught so many palliative medicine – including myself. He has brought inspiration and care to so many countries throughout the world.*

Plate 1   *Fabiola, the holy woman who first named Hospice, as a place of hospitality.*

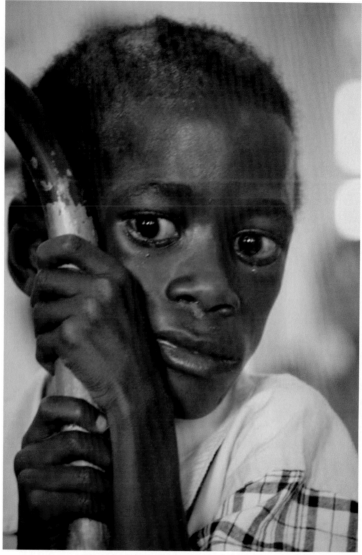

Plate 2 *The total pain of a child. Photo courtesy of Clare Muvaney.*

Plate 3   *The Frangipani tree, whose sap controls the pain of herpes Zoster. This is our emblem of pain control in Africa.*

Plate 4   *Pawpaw seeds dried and crushed make ideal and affordable laxatives.*

Plate 5 *James (not his real name). Left: 2007, with his baby and his tumour. Middle: 2009, having had traditional medicine applied to the tumour. Right: 2010, with the same child, after visiting hospice; he was referred for chemotherapy and is feeling well with a new beginning for life.*

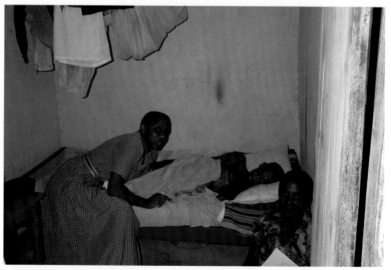

Plate 6 *Martha Rabwoni (MHM) consoling a patient who is dying in his own home where he has chosen to be.*

Plate 8 *Mary McAleese, Irish President, with her husband Martin, signing the visitors book during her visit to Hospice Africa in Makindye, 2001.*

Plate 7 *Dr Jacinto Amandua, Commissioner for Health and our palliative care champion in the Ministry of Health. Photo courtesy of Abby Prabasco.*

Plate 9 *Class of 2009, International Programmes Course for Initiators on the roof in Munyonyo.*

Plate 10   *Sick children singing at Palliative Care Week, 2009.*

Plates 11-13 *Left: Dr Ludovik Zirimenya with patient on a home visit, 2010. Photo courtesy of Abby Prabasco. Top right: two broody volunteers, Tomas and Stu, with my grandchildren, 2010. Right, with Cherie Blair receiving fellowship award, for contributing to relief of pain in the world, 2001.*

Plates 14–17   *Top: Community volunteers for hospice in Makindye, at their annual get together at Makindye, 2010. Top right: the youngest volunteer. Left: Lesley and David Phipps with their two daughters. A family affair since 1992 supporting HA and Uganda. Bottom right: With Jim Bennett (2010). Jim with his wife Jane, was the prime mover behind HA (Soins Palliatifs) France.*

Plate 18   *Children enjoying activities at day care in HAU Makindye, 2010.*

Plate 19   *My family in Munyonyo, Kampala, 2010. Left to right, seated: Margaret Kazibwe, me with Rayan (Margaret's son), Anne Bissaso (Little Anne); standing: Alice, Mary and Molly (Little Anne's children).*

17 Me, Myself . . .

Close your eyes.
Gather all the kindling
About your heart
To create one spark.
That is all you need
To nourish the flame
That will cleanse the dark
Of its weight of festered fear.[37]

HAVING WORKED in several countries I have decided that if I am to be reborn I will come back as an anthropologist. It is so interesting to see how culture, social norms from birth, education and life paths shape the person that we meet today.

Conflict is inevitable, regardless of whether we are talking about ourselves or in relationships to others. The complexity of the human psyche and spirit can be compounded when people come together with distinctly different personalities, communication styles, motives, perspectives and philosophies and yet are trying to reach a common goal. I have been told that people who get things done in this world are often very difficult and I presume it is because they are not 'yes people' and often try to get things moving regardless of others' feelings and have a disregard for keeping to 'social rules'.

In reading about the lives of people who have founded an organisation or even a religious order, we find there is a common denominator running through these lives, whereby after the honeymoon period they are often criticised to the extent that their criticism may undermine the initial work. Some have even died ostracised by the organisation they have founded. But a very important point is that despite

---

[37] John O'Donohue, *Benedictus*, Bantam Press, p. 123 from 'For Courage'.

these frictions, the organisation usually carries on even after the founder has gone, inspiring God's work in this world.

Therefore I write this section about my own personal traits to show how I have learned to deal with those who may hold conflicting opinions from mine in a constructive manner and finding forward movement even in the most trying of times.

I am aware that at times I may appear determined and difficult to deal with. When I believe something is right, particularly in ethical issues and the growth of hospice, although I am prepared to discuss the matter, I will not change my mind unless convinced it is wrong. However, there are many different sides to me, and I was very touched when a young volunteer wrote the following account of me recently.

From a live-in volunteer – the good, the bad and the ugly ...

Dr Anne's diversity in character makes her one of the more intriguing people I have come across. She has a great range of personality traits from one of her most common phrases: 'I am *sooo* angry' to having one of the hugest capacities to care and love for others. I mean on the one hand there is this great idealism, principled and visionary side. This woman has dedicated her entire life to others. Her vision and commitment is beyond ordinary, for few people have sacrificed so selflessly. I am in awe of her heart, faith and the achievements she has been able to accomplish.

But this 'saintlike' side is combined with a very human element. People often find her a challenge to work with. She gets hurt, defensive, angry and can have a short fuse. But don't we all? And it is this side that I find so endearing. In one conversation I asked what helps sustain her through the difficult times? In one of her classic responses combining honesty with her usual wit she said, 'I usually turn to God . . . and just give out stink to him . . . and stink out to everybody around me for that matter.'

I have an enormous amount of respect for her self-awareness and honesty about herself. Another aspect of this woman that I find so amazing is the fun-loving energy she exuberates as a 74 year old. I myself, 24 years, find her more fun and engaging to hang out with than I do most people my own age. I mean here is this lady, a nun for 20 years, dedicating her life to God and the caring of others but she can sit down at night and with good humour watch *Sex and the City* with me. What can I say? She's one of a kind and the world is blessed to have her. (*Six-month volunteer*)

Figure 17.1   *Autumn Fielding, volunteer, who was the catalyst for this book in 2008.*

From my perspective

In order to describe myself, I have to admit, I sought help from a friend who is also a trusted colleague. I was asked to think of five traits, which I couldn't, so instead thought of important but different dynamics of who I am. I am aware, as are many others, of the part of me that is strongly opinionated, intense and tends not to give a damn about what others think. These sometimes endearing qualities have often led to my creating enemies. This occurs particularly when people make ignorant statements about the developing world of which they have little or no experience and I feel it is my duty to set the record straight. I realise later that it may have been a little foolish of me to approach the situation with so little social grace and regard for developing future relationships and contacts and I have to admit that, due to this, I may often appear arrogant to others.

Funnily enough, arrogance is the one quality I can't stand in others! I also find myself knee-deep in conflict when others' values and principles are incongruent with my own and their behaviour lacks integrity. I have no problem letting my opinion be heard on the matter, and although this side of my personality may cause many challenges, it has also made me a strong and competent leader for I am not afraid of the consequences when I believe that what I am doing is right.

Another aspect of who I am was greatly moulded by being a sister for twenty years. I do not regret any of these years! The life of a Medical Missionary of Mary (MMM) nurtured in me a deep spirituality and hospice spirit. My door was always open, especially to those in need. When I first came home after twenty years as an MMM, to our little three-bedroomed 'corpy' (the corporation house where I was born in the upstairs front room) in Liverpool, my mother found my constant flow of friends difficult to deal with as there was nowhere for them to sleep. But by then that was me. Mum had got used to a quiet life, having lived on her own for many years and becoming confined to the house more recently because of her illness.

Figure 17.2
Mother Mary Martin (1892–1983), founded MMM in 1937; she was my greatest inspiration for the hospitality of hospice.

I have a deep respect for life and for the caring of others. I share my house with friends, visitor and volunteers. This is the side from which the hospice ethos has arisen and which I would like to pass on to others before I die. This is where I have totally accepted the ethos of hospitality in my private life and in hospice. My caring is particularly for those who are suffering and I have to say that although I would work tirelessly for hospice, I am terribly aware that there are other forms of suffering in this world. And I must be aware of helping these other organisations. My home in Kampala has been blessed with young women who have looked after me, cared for my friends – and sometimes enemies! And they have been my family over these seventeen years. They have had their children and shared their young lives with me, which has brought me untold joy and happiness.

In my later years I've been invited to speak to many different audiences around the world. One gift of my personality enables me to bring the needs of the suffering in stark reality to the audience and has been a boon for advocacy. It enables me to be a confidante for people in trouble. I also realise that if I can't feel my own wounds I cannot help the wounded. Being hurt is almost the flip side of helping the hurt.

Another aspect of my personality is a crazy, adventurous side which makes me open to new experiences and allows me to approach life as a happy, fearless youngster. I had to agree with my friend that sometimes I am prepared to venture where others do not dare to tread. Perhaps it has something to do with not having the worries of an immediate family. I remember when threatened with death in Ethiopia when I was younger, I was not afraid of dying but the worry it would give my mother. But now that I am single and fancy free I am possibly more daring than I've ever been. This is very helpful in moving through other African countries. I am very aware that in present-day Africa we can never be sure what will happen next, and a position of safety may very quickly mutate into one of danger.

I believe in being open to new things. I believe I inherited this from my mother. I would like to think of myself as someone who is open and aware of the way the world is moving today. Thus, I was particularly hurt when I was accused of having 'founder syndrome':

> This phenomenon often occurs after the initial growth of a non profit organisation, when the mission evolves beyond what its founder originally had in mind. This creates conflict between newcomers, who want the organisation to adapt and the founder, who wants to keep things the way they were.[38]

The word 'syndrome' indicates a sickness. Granted, I am a founder, but in today's world founders tend to fail if they are not prepared to move with the rapid changes in our world and always be ready to take on

---

[38] Wikipedia, 2008.

new challenges along with new developments. However, there is a need for integrity, always ensuring that new developments are for the good of the patient and family and not for another agenda.

Another obstacle that I have faced is the challenge of implementing change as a woman. Women have come a long way but still have a long way to go in gaining equal footing with men. Hence, I have found it quite difficult, especially in Africa where men tend to be dominant, have a stronger voice and be given more respect. But for me the bottom line is that I find it very irritating and hurtful when, regardless of gender, there is a lack of respect. Lack of respect for our ethos is even more hurtful when it is denied and put down by people close to us, even considered part of us.

I am intolerant of people who want to 'teach their grandmother to suck eggs'. To have to sit in front of a person and be lectured on something they just recently learned on the internet, while I have learned it through blood, sweat and tears over the last seventy-five years, can leave me exasperated. Being old is not easy, especially when the world no longer respects the wisdom gained from an entire life's experiences. Youngsters may think they have the answers to everything and no longer try to gain knowledge from those who have gone before them. Yet I have a great belief in the youngsters of today and how they are going to change the world: so many have given of themselves, helping the less fortunate. I have to listen to them!

But even worse is when a person tries to take the heart out of hospice. Now this may be done unintentionally but because of the amount of power their positions may command such as being a board member or heading the organisation, it is even more critical for them to lead with sincere and careful thought. As leaders we need to be aware of our example and the ripple effects our actions and words may create. These insensitivities and unthoughtful moments have not only hurt me but the team as well and of course then our patients suffer. These situations are hard to cope with, but of course, I approach them head on and often get hurt or make mistakes. But as always we must try to learn from them, make the best of them, even build on them and move on.

Also the cultural aspects of conflict must be understood. In my African experience, people can sometimes feel intimidated and over-fearful of authority. Often this may be associated with the fear of someone putting a spell on them – yes, this is still believed.

Figure 17.3 *I have a great belief in the youngsters of today:*
Hannah Merriman, volunteering in 2010,
with Rayan.

Interactions become more complex as we grow in numbers. We need to be brave and aware and ready to stand up for what is right. Power and financial gain often run hand in hand. We doctors are often in danger of succumbing to these pressures. People in positions of authority are often so proud. Your value is held to derive more from the amount you earn than the amount you give. Yet it is the givers that move the care of the patients forward.

Me and my God

The last part I will expand on is the spiritual aspect of who I am. God has been a part of my life from childhood. My God, this greater being, has been my soulmate from childhood. I now feel he is part of me, someone I can turn to in joy and sorrow, someone I can turn to when confronted with suffering in others and someone who will also be there for me no matter what. This might be compared to a relationship between partners but the difference is that my vision of God has no failures. This is not always easy to justify, but there it is.

Although this relationship is very strong for me, I don't always revert to it in times of stress. As my temper begins rising, I often forget to turn to God until reflecting later. It is only afterwards that I realise that the source of my peace was left behind. Keeping equilibrium in such circumstances can be difficult; I hope my readers know what I'm talking about.

Bishop Kevin's talk to us about 'centring prayer' was confirmation of what I had been doing my entire life. Especially as I get older, the ability to centre myself has been a great source of consolation and provided peace in times of great turmoil. I often turn to this practice when I reflect on times in my life when I was desperately upset and didn't know which way to turn. I can now see that through the pain and confusion God was leading me in a certain direction. Born a Catholic and still a Catholic, my spirituality has gone beyond what I learned on my mother's knee or in the Catholic Church. But I think reflection on our life path is a special grace for older people, one of the few blessings of old age in this world today.

Having been a sister for twenty years (and then not one for thirty-seven years) I realise the vital role on the formation of my personality and values of my life that occurred during those twenty years. As a youngster I found too many things to distract me, I was unfocused but just enjoyed life as it unfolded, giving more priority to the enjoyment of the present moment than to hard work. It was the joyful spirit of the MMMs that created an environment in which I developed great discipline and focus, enabling me to pursue medicine. I do not regret any part of those twenty years for they have made me who I am. Looking back over the years since, I can see there was a path, a light that brought me to the commencement of Hospice Africa.

My personality today makes me want to see things through and to ensure that what we start has an outcome. This may be donor talk, but in fact it was there all along from Hospice Africa.

Dealing with conflict

Along with the good comes the bad. I realise that the contradicting dynamics and often challenging aspects of who I am have been a catalyst in the development of hospice. Thus I must accept who I am and how it has affected the ways in which I have dealt with other individuals and how I handle myself in adverse situations. I have felt the brunt of people who have found me difficult more in the last five years than in the first ten years. But I must accept that I played a vital role in this conflict and move on. For often it is through conflict and challenges that growth and progress are made.

> *There is a crack in everything ...*
> *That's how the light gets in ...*
> (Leonard Cohen, 'Anthem', 1992)

18 New Initiatives, Donor Experience in Africa

Money is better than poverty, if only for financial reasons.
Woody Allen

WHEN YOU ARE as long in the tooth as I am, you have seen fashions come and go and then the same thing comes into fashion some years later. This is as true in the donor scene as in the fashion industry and medicine.

Today many organisations are 'donor-driven'. This means that they have to follow 'donor-speak'. Donor-speak changes from year to year and their favourite words change along with it. The present ones that come to mind that were never on the list before are:

1. *advocacy* – this has always been there but it was just plain speaking, and selling the needs of patients and families, and publishing newsletters; today it is a budget line

2. *challenges* – no one has problems any more!

3. *outcomes* – previously we just got on with what was needed; today we behave as if we are in complete control of what is going to happen in the future; we are not!

4. *five-year or ten-year plans* and hope to reach our …

5. … *targets* within certain times but we haven't taken in …

6. … *the X factor* – that factor which works in spite of us to meet the needs presented by changing circumstances.

But donors have money, and money in today's world is power. And sometimes that power makes people think that they know everything because donors do not usually have people living and working in the countries they seek to help. They need to work in partnership with the people on the ground. They need to befriend the people on the ground so that they just don't get the answers required by the donors far away in another continent, but will know honestly what works and what doesn't. It is only through working with people on the ground in the country that they will see through false claims and outcomes which are so easily put on paper. Some donors take this seriously and actually visit sites themselves to see what is going on the ground. But even then it is very difficult to absorb many years' work in one day's visit.

HAU has suffered many humiliations from donors, giving the impression that they know it all. Palliative care is a new concept in medicine for donors and those on the ground alike. This has made it quite painful to approach some donors and if we don't jump when they ask us to jump it can make life quite difficult. A regular donor who was approached for further funding actually told us we should close Mobile Hospice Mbarara (MHM). When I thought of all the heartache and generosity that had been put into MHM to make it the excellent service it is today, I was truly gobsmacked! This person who had never visited was telling us to close it, advising us to reduce the services, believing he could advise on this because he held the purse strings of that organisation. This left me very hurt. We need the donor but the donor needs us too!

Sadly, an approach that does not build on the past experiences can do harm to the donors themselves. Most of all, by not building on experience in Africa, we can harm our patients and families. It is so important that the right persons are employed by donor organisations, to work in these sensitive situations. One person with a self-centred approach can destroy any donor organisation or the organisation on the ground. But we on the ground need to discern if bad vibes are coming from one person and not put down a whole organisation that is appreciating our work and has supported us well.

Sometimes when asking for funds we feel as if the donor thinks we are asking for money to put into our own pockets. There is often a lack of respect for our expertise and for the work that has been done to help the patient and family. As an example, on one occasion we were left waiting for an appointment by a businessman in Kampala. Even though we had the appointment, he walked in and then out, without explaining or apologising. As far as he was concerned we were beggars and he was rich and we were seeking money for the poor. This is very hurtful but it is also taking care away from the patients because it is often the doctor or the nurse who have left their work with patients to come to the meeting. It is very frustrating to think that the patient is denied care while we try to help them.

Figure 18.1 *Little Hospice Hoima (LHH) staff: From left to right, starting with the back row: Deo Nesige, John Kisembo, James Kivumbi, Martin Agaba, Isaac Katabalwa, Stephen Byaruhanga, Innocent Kahuma, Rosemary Nsimenta, Robert Kyomuhendo, Betty Kasigwa, Irene Mbabazi, Erina Kyomuhendo. Kneeling: Hannah Merriman and Anne Falster.*

I pray that the spirit of hospitality within our hospices in Africa will flourish and grow. This demands that we respect each other, recognise initiatives that grow from a selfless love of the patient, usually from the people on the ground, and take them on board. It means seeing the good in each other and nourishing our new members so that they can grow in the knowledge that they will be heard and respected as they bring new ideas. It means discerning selflessness and moving away from the self-centred. I pray for discernment in all those who carry forward this great mission that we are privileged to be part of.

We have been given a huge responsibility to carry this flame which can so easily be extinguished in the efforts to be distinguished.

Figure 18.2 *Catherine Nawangi washes a patient's wounds at home.*

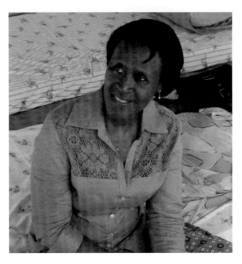

Figure 18.3 *Catherine Ruwambaya, volunteer coordinator
at HAU for ten years.*

19 Brain Drain, Costing and Clinical Standards

Money is only loaned to a man.
He comes into the world with nothing
and he leaves with nothing.[39]

BRAIN DRAIN is a problem everywhere in Africa. And I can hear you all saying it's the same in England and Ireland . . . This is a phenomenon worldwide where the call to help the suffering is being replaced by the need for riches. In developing countries within Africa, as elsewhere, people understandably look for bigger and better salaries. Traditional values in the villages are rapidly being changed, particularly for those fortunate enough to obtain university education. They now see a world where money speaks and money influences and can dictate to others. Money is power. They see government officials not content with their comparatively huge salaries taking bribes and practising other corrupt practices.

All Africans want the best for their children. So when their salaries increase, the children go to better schools. If the salary stops, the children can no longer go to these better schools so they even move abroad out of their own country to take jobs with remuneration that will cover their high expectations for education for their children along with their other expectations for life.

However, the brain drain has left countries like Malawi with no stable group of doctors to carry through a service. They rely mainly on clinical officers. In Uganda the doctor to patient ratio is 1:19,000 whereas in UK it is 1:450. Yet the medical schools have been producing up to 200 doctors a year, and more and more medical schools are now opening. Abroad these doctors receive excellent training and many stay in the country of their specialist training and are considered excellent doctors.

---

[39] William Crapo Durant, Founder of General Motors and Chevrolet.

Figure 19.1 *It is hard to keep dedicated team members. Palliative Care Nurse Jerith (left) on a home visit in LHH.*

We all agree that medical personnel have low salaries in African countries. However in Uganda today the salaries have increased greatly over the last fifteen years. Once a health professional is trained in palliative care they are highly marketable as palliative care is now a buzzword among donors. Many are attracted away from the service to patients to take administrative posts with high salaries, usually paid for by organisations funded by the West. Indeed the West is very responsible for the brain drain because many overseas governments have come in offering salaries without checking out the realities within the countries themselves.

For the first ten years of Hospice Africa we were lucky enough to be able to maintain a core staff and we were training people into senior positions to take over from any expats. However, we did have a brain drain from 1998 when the Mildmay Centre for Palliative Care of HIV/AIDS patients, seeking Ugandan staff trained in palliative care, became a source of higher salaries; hence we lost several of our staff. Later with the development of the African Palliative Care Association (APCA) (developed from our third objective and in utero at hospice for two years before moving into their own office in 2005) a significant brain drain occurred of the very people we were training for key posts in our expanding organisation.

It is common in Uganda that when people apply for posts and come to interview they ask the new organisation not to give the information that they have applied to the organisation they are working for. This is understandable because if they don't get the post they may well be discriminated against for wanting to leave the original organisation. Within the country of Uganda, people often stay in the same post for many years if not for life.

However, career development is very important for team members in palliative care. This may mean they are moving through networking organisations, sharing experiences, and being better people themselves. Networking organisations such as HAU, Mildmay, APCA, PCAU should be mature enough to discuss with each other, with team members potentially moving between organisations to gain further experiences. Key personnel may improve by moving amongst networking organisations, keeping in mind the best for their own development and that the care for patients and families is the best for everybody. This would be a sign of maturity for organisations.

Hospice Africa Uganda, being the first to bring palliative care into Uganda and having trained people in a new specialty, has suffered most from the brain drain by networking organisations. This was understandable initially but was not expected. Thus my reaction to the moving of team members, who were the hope for our own future, was anger for them and the networking organisations that did not share their aspirations with us. It was only presented to us when finalised and the person was moving into a new contract with a new organisation. This anger, I now realise, was misplaced and I take it more calmly these days. But as part of our ethos for African Hospice and Palliative Care, I am disappointed when we are not honest and up front with each other.

The other side of the equation of course is that hospice has declared that it wants to be affordable and culturally acceptable to the whole of Africa. Uganda is now in the middle-income group of the Human Development Index,[40] whereas most African countries are in the lower-income group. If we are to be a model for that, we have to keep our care for patients affordable, but the cost towards the patients increases with an increase in team members' salaries. So, although our salaries are a little

---

[40] UNDP Human Development Index, 2008

above that of the Ministry of Health, they are still low compared to some other NGOs and international organisations. This is a hard line to define and to tread: sustaining and retaining our team members. Maintaining a balance between having qualified team members and keeping our services affordable is a recurring dilemma.

Of course it is not just being qualified that is required of hospice team members. These members need to be inspirational themselves to be carried along by their belief in the ethos and to be able to be seen to have fire in their belly. This fire develops from the conviction that what they are doing is contributing to the availability of human rights of people to be free of suffering. It gives them the courage to stand up for what they believe in and to advocate not only within Uganda but to Africa and the rest of the world. We now have in Africa individuals marked out as belonging to the FBB (Fire in the Belly Brigade!) These people are essential in moving the frontiers of hospice so that it reaches everybody in need in Africa.

Costing today in HAU

From an annual cost of £24,000 (€28,000, US$35,000) per year in 1993, we are now using £1 million (€1.2M, US$1.5M) per year and this is increasing. At the moment, approximately half of all funding is for patient care and just less than half goes to our education programmes. Education is most important because those we train, both in Uganda and from other African countries, will see more and more patients and bring relief and peace. Thus we do not intend to increase the numbers of patients we see, but assist those we train with the most difficult cases.

The present cost of care is 22,000 Ugandan shillings (£7, €8 or US$10) per patient per week. This is an average for all our patients across the three sites. Patients are seen at hospice or visited usually once per week. However it may be more or less, according to their condition and needs. Patients are asked to pay 5000 Ugandan shillings per week (£1.70, €2 or US$2.5) towards this cost, independent of the number of visits and medications. About one-third of our patients can manage to pay. We assist those who cannot afford (60%). We visit our patients and families at home, supporting them with pain and symptom control and counselling. This cost includes transport and specially trained staff.

As we expand and have more buildings, maintenance costs come into play, as well as the replacement of expensive consumables like computers and cars.

Morphine is our greatest contribution to Uganda and to Africa. A plastic (recycled water) bottle of 500 mls solution, containing 500 mgs of morphine powder with preservative and a dye, costs only the price of a loaf of bread. This is 1500 Ugandan shillings or about £0.50, €0.60 or US$0.70. This lasts our average patient 10 days including extra doses for breakthrough pain. This is cheaper than aspirin or paracetamol. This is the strength of 5 mgs per 5 mls and we colour it green.

We also make up 50 mgs per 5 mls which is coloured pink, and 100 mgs per 5 ml which is blue. The stronger the solution the cheaper the cost price because the preservative is more costly than the morphine powder. The present preservative (bronopol) gives a shelf life of three months but in Ethiopia they are researching bronopol plus sodium peroxide, which they estimate may give a shelf life of six months. However, our patients use it very quickly. In Ethiopia only 15% access a health worker and people are in pain far away from the capital, Addis Ababa. So they may need to take up to three months' supply with them with instructions for use.

Those who are interested in more facts on costing and donors are referred to the website (www.hospiceafrica.or.ug) where they can access the monthly fact sheet and the Annual Report.

Patient coverage and standards

From our work in Uganda and with other African countries, we estimate that a new programme should not have more than 30 patients per health professional (including doctor, clinical officers, nurses and dispenser) or 20 patients per team member (which also includes the support staff such as drivers and administration). If there are more than this, then the quality of the service deteriorates. This is because our work is time intensive and we need time to listen to our patients and understand their problems in a holistic way.

You can see from Table 12.1, taken from the April 2010 fact sheet, that Mobile Hospice Mbarara are seeing almost as many patients as Kampala, with much fewer clinical members in the team. However, as palliative care is time-intensive, this is not ideal. As stated, there ideally should not be more than 30 patients per health professional. Although the discrepancy between Mbarara and Kampala figures can be explained by the nature of their follow-up roadside clinics and outreaches, it is still not ideal and there is a great need for us to employ and train more nurses. However MHM has a logistical problem in that the hospice site is too small and there is not enough space for increased team members. This is presently being rectified as we prepare to move the hospice in the next few years to a larger site and a new building.

As the team members increase, staff costs increase in proportion. The year 2008-09 shows that staff costs are approximately 40% versus the service costs which are about 60%.

Volunteerism, salaries and leaders

In my own lifetime, volunteerism has changed tremendously. Volunteers coming through agencies such as VSO and Peace Corps came on a minimal salary and generously gave their services. Sadly, today many overseas personnel are demanding as much as they would get in their own countries and sometimes even more. I feel that this has affected the 'fire in the belly', or enthusiastic approach, as a centre of care. If our motive is to help others but the help for others is given only in proportion to the remuneration that we would like, then we have lost something.

However, I agree that the world is changing and we have to move on to what is occurring. In many countries, even African countries, money is becoming the god. But we have to work with the materials we have available. The result of this mental rummaging brings us to a bottom line of this discussion. Yes, fire in the belly is necessary but today more than ever it needs fuelling with the higher salaries. In looking at common denominators both in our own organisation and others, to make a new initiative a success it requires at least one person with fire in the belly. Sometimes it does matter how much money and training you put into its people and you need a leader who will be willing to move it forward and face opposition, secure in the knowledge of the needs of patients and families and referring everything back to the fact that all we do is to improve the lot of the suffering.

20 Hospice Africa Worldwide and the Struggle for Funding

Genuine community is always characterised by integrity.[41]

TRYING TO RAISE funds when an organisation is still a vision and not off the ground is very difficult. We experienced this in the years before 1993 and the first few years of Hospice Africa Uganda.

Early years: Ireland and UK

In 1992, I visited Ireland with a view to getting support for Hospice Africa. At the time Uganda had not been selected as the model. We needed funding for the feasibility study and we needed it fast. So I approached the Ministry of Foreign Affairs with the view of getting a grant from Irish Aid. Although Irish Aid required applications several months in advance they were very interested in our proposed work and advised me to seek assistance from the Irish Civil Society Fund housed in the same building. The Civil Society Fund comes from donations collected from salaries of the civil service employees. They told me that they would consider giving us a small grant to do the feasibility study. This resulted in our first grant of 4000 punts (Irish pounds) which enabled Fazal and me to carry it out in early 1993.

I also visited the Agency for Personal Services Overseas (APSO). The lady I had most dealings with at that time was Gretchen Fitzgerald, of Asian origin and married to an Irish, who told me to come back when we knew what country we were going to start in. Gretchen was so helpful to us and I was saddened by her premature death from cancer in 2001. One of my main worries at that time was how I would live and be funded when working in the African country which would be the model.

---

[41] M. Scott Peck, *The Different Drum*, Simon & Schuster, 1987, p. 234.

Following the feasibility study, I went back to APSO and told them we had selected Uganda. APSO works through registered charities in developed countries. But we had not yet registered. So they suggested I worked through another organisation registered in Ireland or the UK. Because of my personal relations with the MMMs we approached them for their help. This was agreed and funding commenced that year, 1993.

Meanwhile we were advised to approach another organisation in Ireland, the Irish National Teachers Organisation (INTO). This was interested in funding education and training in the developing world and together with the Scottish Catholic International Aid Fund (SCIAF), and the Catholic Fund for Overseas Development (CAFOD), INTO funded our initial training programmes in Uganda.

SCIAF was visited in 1993 after the feasibility study; they too were interested in the expansion of making palliative care available through education. They asked me to write a proposal and a budget. I did so and went up to see them. Of course, I had had no training or experience in writing proposals and my mathematics on the budget were hopeless! The lady in charge sat me down and went through the budget with me step by step and taught me some lessons which have remained with me to this day. However, I thought, they will never work with a *dumbo* like me! Far from it, they too recognised vision and they funded education up to 2000, until the Diana Fund came in.

HA (UK)

Hospice Africa UK, now off the ground, had been mainly led and organised by Lesley Phipps. I have talked about her and her husband previously, but the work could not have carried on without her continuous support; she was then working full time on the emergency social work team in Liverpool. On the boards of UK and Uganda she has been an important link. From the earliest days, she took an interest in the team members as well as the patients and families. Many of the earlier team members remember her as their confidante in problems and as a bridge to mend difficulties at hospice and sometimes also in their personal lives. If I am the *JaaJaa*, Lesley is that special aunt in which all can confide. Thus over the years she has had a unique insight into the culture of Uganda and the history and progress of HAU and hospices in Africa.

In the early years donors came and went and at the same time Hospice Africa commenced covenanting amongst people in the UK which has allowed us to have non-restricted funding which is needed so often as costs increase and gaps appear in our budgets. Lesley was the person fronting the proposals and the budgets and has a very good name with donors as she always delivers.

The Catholic Association for Overseas Development (CAFOD) is based in London and raises funding for their overseas programmes during the Friday Fast scheme in the Catholic Church. They were a great support to us in the first years and particularly during the time of setting up Mobile Hospice Mbarara (MHM). They remained our friends over the years, agreeing to be a fallback if we had problems with funding. In the last twelve months they have renewed their association with us, applying for co-funding with other organisations such as Comic Relief.

Having obtained the funding for the feasibility study in 1993 from the Civil Society of Ireland, we realised while visiting the countries in Africa, the great and varied needs in each country. It was obvious that little funding would be availed for palliative care services within an African country.

Uganda

One of the reasons for lack of support, including financial support in palliative care in Africa, is that although everybody dies, the prevention of diseases, particularly in the under-fives, is a much greater priority than caring for those who are dying from communicable and non-communicable disease. We came to Uganda with the objective of bringing palliative care and caring for those with cancer. By our second year we actually worked out the best approach to take towards AIDS patients, by adapting methods that worked with our experiences with cancer and applying them to pain and symptoms in HIV/AIDS. Although this was working well, when our methods were offered in an article for publication in a UK tropical medicine journal we were informed that these methods had not been recognised or published in the UK as yet, so they could not be published!

From then on we have managed many patients. However, although we still only care for cancer and/or HIV/AIDS patients, through our training we are teaching palliative care to be adaptable to any disease and any end-of-life situation.

In 1993, raising funds for cancer patients, whether they had HIV or cancer, was almost impossible. The donor climate was for prevention. As stated earlier, I was told in the USA that if I was looking for condoms there would be no problems with funding but because I was looking for care there were no donors. They were dying anyway so let them die. There was a lack of recognition and sympathy for these people who were dying in severe pain without medical care.

When governments are looking for funding, cancer is not amongst their priorities. This is because cancer is not amongst the top ten causes of death except perhaps in South Africa. The top ten causes of death are all infections including TB and malaria, but most infections today in Africa are caused by low immunity. Of course you never see HIV or AIDS on a death certificate, but then you rarely see death certificates either in Africa. Many people die at home and 57% of the population in Uganda never sees a health worker. Cancer is low down on the priority whereas if you mention HIV in your application for funding, either from government or an NGO, funds arrive on your doorstep. This is why we have thousands of organisations in Uganda with 'AIDS' in the title.

In latter years we have gained from the funding coming from the US President's Emergency Plan for AIDS Relief (PEPFAR) for palliative care. But in the early days we really struggled for money, so where did we get it?

Hospice Africa UK, France and the charity shops

Hospice Africa UK was registered in June 1993 to raise and receive funds from UK sources. However, this small group of people also got together to open the first charity shop. This was mainly through the efforts of one of the early board members, Alice Davidson, who with her family set up the shop. Two members of the original team have been running the shop ever since. Initially in rent-free premises and staffed completely by volunteer old-age pensioners, they were raising £2000 a month in 1994 which almost met our needs at that point. In the years 1993–94 we were running on £24,000 a year (one small site and three employees); today it costs £1 million a year to run the expanded services of Hospice Africa (three hospice sites and 135 employees).

The first shop was in Old Swan, Liverpool. The initial premises were moved several times. The second premises were in Prescot Road, Liverpool, which is a main road. They were there for five years and then moved to the current premises, about 500 yards from the previous premises. Regular customers followed their shop. The shop is still coordinated by Pete and Anne Purcell who will sell anything from a tin plate to a fur coat. Often factories will donate overstocked items. All of these are at affordable prices and the shop is popular with the local community. However, it is difficult to have continuity of personnel working in the shop due to the age group of the volunteers. But there is great support amongst the team and they support each other through their life events.

Figure 20.1   *90-year-old Marge celebrates her birthday in the charity shop at Old Swan, Liverpool; right: Ann and Pete Purcell.*

The second shop was opened in Ainsdale, a more affluent area outside Liverpool, in 1995. Because it was not on the main road it took a while to build up its clientele. The other initial problem was that it was only open part-time because of the lack of volunteers, but after Lesley Phipps took over as coordinator, the shop turned out to be equally popular and now has great support.

Both of these shops offer a tremendous service and give us a backbone support to our funding needs. The money raised is unrestricted and can be used for any need. Hospice is constantly having needs that don't fit into budget lines. The volunteers do not ask for anything and they enjoy themselves in helping the people. Hospice Africa UK ensures they are able to attend the UK AGM so they can get to know each other and see the difference their contribution has made to the patients and families in Africa, as well as to their local community.

Visitors to HA (UK), especially from Africa, are encouraged to visit these shops just to see the dedication of these teams. The Old Swan shop recently celebrated the 90th birthday of one of our long-term volunteers!

Lesson: to stay young and live long, work in a charity shop!

However discussing the charity shops would be incomplete without telling of our latest charity shop commenced in 2009 by Hospice Africa (Soins Palliatifs) France. This is in Brittany and is being supported by a large number of expatriate British who have settled there. Many of these are retired but in a younger age group than the Liverpool and Ainsdale shops. Their generosity has to be seen to be believed and during my recent visit I was really impressed with their great enthusiasm. This newest registered Hospice Africa branch is for the establishment of a model in Francophone Africa.

Jim Bennett and his wife Jane are the prime movers behind HA (Soins Palliatifs) France. They are long-term supporters and friends of HAU ever since I met Jim in the street in Jersey in 1999. Ann Bailhache, who was then President of the Jersey Overseas Aid Commission, introduced me to Jim as someone who wanted to help in the developing world, having just retired at an earlier age than usual. Following the usual interviews and exchange of experiences, Jim first came to Uganda to assist with our accounts in 2000. He has continued to assist ever since and understands our accounting systems and controls very well.

Jim and Jane, who he since married, are now settled in Brittany, engaged in their hobby of producing and acting plays and running HA France.

The Diana Fund and HAU

Where do we fit into the donors in the world today when the majority of funding is going to HIV/AIDS? Our relationships with different donors often arose from the ethos of hospitality. Several people from donor agencies have enjoyed our hospitality both in hospice and in my home. This has enabled us to discuss our issues and promote our work. However, we have met the occasional donors who are not allowed to accept hospitality from those to whom they donate. The one that springs to mind is the Diana, Princess of Wales Memorial Fund. And although we have had time to discuss matters formally, they have missed out on one aspect of hospitality which is so essential for our ethos.

Figure 20.2 *Jim Bennett in the French charity shop.*

I had been in UK when they announced the tragic death of Diana, Princess of Wales. I had watched her care for those less fortunate and her special relationship with the hospice world. The grief of the British people was poured into the Diana, Princess of Wales Memorial Fund.

In 2000, the Fund was looking for an organisation in Africa that could assist them in offering financial assistance for palliative care in African countries. They did their homework on the internet and decided we were the organisation with a mission close to their own at the time and I was invited to meet them the next time I was in London. This was one of the 'wow's in the life of hospice funding.

I met two of the leading ladies working there, Anne Lloyd-Williams and Olivia Dix, for lunch at a Chinese restaurant. After enjoying a wonderful meal and sharing our experiences, the restaurant gave us fortune cookies. I read mine and announced to the table: 'You are about to come into a fortune'!

Both ladies looked amazed and then started to laugh. Then and there they requested that HA partner with the Diana Fund. After discussing the work, it was then that the news was broken to me that they were offering to give us £100,000 annually for three years in order for us to bring palliative care to other African countries and to support our training programmes including the new Diploma in Palliative Medicine with Makerere University and an educational resource centre for Africa on site in Makindye, Kampala.

This was a moment of great joy for me. Not only were we receiving the largest donation we had ever had, but I had met a group of dedicated people with a mission close to our own. I remember buying a picture postcard of Princess Diana on the way back to Battersea where I was staying with my brother and the Salesian community in Battersea. I was walking on air – the founding mission of Hospice Africa and the third objective of Hospice Africa Uganda, to support palliative care in other African countries, had not only become a reality (begun in 2000) but now had secure financial backing for three years.

Our friends in the Diana, Princess of Wales Memorial Fund also explained that as this was their first venture into palliative care in Africa, they would learn greatly from us. We shared a lot. Anne Lloyd-Williams was to become our great supporter and was alongside me in Botswana when we first discussed the possibility of a palliative care association for Africa. She has been an advisor from time to time since. Then, later we were to meet Faith Mwangi Powell, a Kenyan lady married to a Welshman. Faith was very much with us and was to share with me her dream to return to Africa and continue to move palliative care there. Faith was the founder CEO for APCA and has really moved this organisation. The Diana Fund are still supporting some of our education activities, but the bonding when people come together to move a concept has lessened. However, we will always remember the initial bonding we had in those early years and the effect it had on the spread of palliative care in Africa.

Palliative care associations

PCAU

The Palliative Care Association of Uganda was launched by Hospice Africa Uganda in 1999 as a consortium of volunteers from the various organisations working in different aspects of palliative care and as a kind of alumni for those who had received training in palliative care in

Uganda. This was the first country palliative care team in Africa above South Africa and as such was really a model.

Figure 20.3 *Anne Lloyd-Williams (left) with Dr Lydia Mpanga Sebuyira at the meeting in Cape Town where the African Palliative Care Association was conceived.*

Figure 20.4 *Rose Kiwanuka, my first Nurse and the country Director of PCAU. Photo courtesy of Abby Prabasco.*

In January 2006, the first office was opened under the direction of Rose Kiwanuka, my first nurse at Hospice Africa Uganda. We were so sad to lose Rose because she has proved herself a great worker, with the hospice spirit and ethos at the heart of all she does for the patients of Uganda. It was at a time when we had lost people to the higher paying organisations and needed her. But looking back, she has done more for palliative care in Uganda in her role as the Country Director of the new organisation. It has been sad to see her struggling for funding, managing the first palliative care association in Africa, yet completely strapped for money, while those more recently started in other countries are mainly funded well and have many more in their teams. Rose still moved ahead with the assistance of a secretary for four years.

PCAU is an organisation to unify and give vision to all those practising support and palliative care in Uganda. Through this organisation we are in touch with many of those who have worked with us for some years and moved on and I am delighted to see them carrying forward the torch and even commencing new initiatives.

Rose's responsibilities include following up those who have been trained in palliative care throughout the country. This she does without a car, moving mainly on public transport, which is difficult when you consider the terrains she has to travel to visit the villages in the districts. More recently she has, with the help of a grant from the Diana Fund, carried out an assessment of those who have been trained and the extent of palliative care practice in Uganda.

This year she has moved to PCAU premises, has been give a vehicle to reach all the Districts of Uganda and is increasing her team.

APCA

In 2003, the first office of the African Palliative Care Association was in Hospice Africa Uganda premises. The initial steering committee was working from there and met regularly under the leadership of HAU. In 2004, Faith, our friend working in the Diana Fund, approached me to say that she was interested in the post of CEO for the new organisation. We were at that time planning our first APCA conference for all Africa to take place in Arusha in 2004. Her line manager at the Fund was not happy about seeing Faith move on but she did after some negotiations and has proved a dedicated advocate for palliative care in Africa, throughout the world.

2004 was a very busy year for us. The steering committee of pre-APCA organised a conference which was to be funded from money that had been promised but which still had not reached us even at the start of the conference. This was a big worry to Mark Jacobson who was organising logistics in Arusha and to ourselves working in Kampala. The money to support this conference had been promised from the USA, and still had not arrived a week before the conference was due to begin. The hotel was threatening to pull out. So Hospice Africa came in and saved the day, transferring the funding and allowing this amazing meeting to go forward. Thus Hospice Africa was involved not only with the founding of APCA but in the initial financial support as part of our founding mission.

After Arusha, I spent a lot of time finding a house suitable for the APCA office and housing for Faith and her family. In January 2005 they came and settled in, and in the last five years have made a great impact in Africa.

Over the three years (2000–03) of the Diana Fund grant, Dr Jack Jagwe, our Senior Advisor in National Policy, and I visited Ethiopia (twice), Tanzania, Malawi, Zambia, Nigeria and Cameroon and assessed their needs. We also introduced the possibility of including palliative medicine into the university undergraduate training for their doctors of tomorrow and also into the curriculum of nurses and clinical officers. All of these countries are now using oral morphine, but to a lesser degree than needed for the many suffering in their countries.

APCA has taken over much of the coordination of training and research aspects of our work, including unifying of services. However, Hospice Uganda continues as the model for Hospice Africa to support new initiatives with clinical input, training on the ground and, when possible, kick-starting funding. Having lived through a period when it was so difficult to get help and the experience of starting up three new hospices and services and introducing the training programmes for small hospices, we have still a lot to give to extend the coverage in Africa.

The Diana Fund meanwhile supported some of the funding for the first Distance Learning Diploma (DLD) in palliative care for Africa and we are most grateful to them for this. This has continued up to today.

My house is your home: hospitality from the heart

The initial house in Muyenga was rented with a view to housing the hospice as well. This did not happen as Henry Mary Kateregga lent us his house in Ndebba. It was therefore large enough to offer hospitality to friends and some of the donors who required accommodation during their time in Uganda. One of our early experiences of this was a visit from a consultant who was out on behalf of a Catholic organisation in Holland. At that time it was called CEBEMO, but today, after several changes of name over the years, it is called CORDAID. The consultant was a German lady who was particularly interested in end-of-life care and as such she came to visit the hospice. She was actually staying quite near to my home in a hotel. She developed an illness while she was in the hotel and I took her to my house and looked after her. From then on she became a great friend to hospice personally and through her organisation. She brought out the Director of CEBEMO and this was one of our early sources of grants which carries on up to today.

Grants from government overseas aid

In overall giving, the largest grants have come from overseas aid programmes from Ireland, Jersey and US. Mildmay (Mildmay Centre for Palliative Care of HIV/AIDS Patients) came into Uganda five years after us with a huge grant from the then UK ODA (Overseas Development Administration) now called DFID (Department for International Development). This relationship with the British Government brought a strong relationship with the Ugandan Government and brought them their influential Patron, President Museveni, the President of Uganda. They came to assist with the HIV/AIDS epidemic and that of course, in itself, attracted assistance for them. Mildmay are doing tremendous work with those affected and infected by HIV and their families. Perhaps this is why DFID has not supported hospice. Although we manage AIDS patients with pain control and illness at the end of life in the home, hospice work is still mostly with cancer patients.

Singapore

Although not such a huge donor as it was at the start, Singapore has continued to support us, both with encouragement and sending out parcels for the children. A small group there, in a very humble way, have collected items for us and every year send out an amount to support the work. I know these individually and like our pensioners in the shops in Liverpool, they are giving from their hearts.

Ireland

Our first donations through Irish Aid came though APSO which was similar to VSO in the UK. They sent specialists to advise us and give us support as required for expatriate volunteers. For example, Micheal McGoldrick was our pharmacist for two years (1995–97). Micheal was the first to make up morphine on the hospice site. Previously it was made up in Nsambya Hospital pharmacy. We oriented the kitchen in the house to be a pharmacy, putting locks on the kitchen cupboard doors and creating a double-locked cupboard for morphine storage. The books for recording meticulously, according to international regulations, were compiled. During his time he set up a computer system for recording the use of all medications and producing labels.

Micheal not only looked after the pharmacy but helped us in many other ways. One of the things he did was to collect the cash from the bank in his own private and unmarked car. This is a fairly dangerous thing in a country where there are a lot of poor people but also a lot of criminals watching *m'zungus*! One day, coming from the bank, he noticed a car following him. He swung into the hospice compound and the car followed. He still thought it was a patient. Suddenly the driver got out and pointed a gun at him. He demanded the money he had just withdrawn from the bank. Luckily, Micheal was a quick thinker and immediately handed it over, the car left with the money, and Micheal lived to tell the tale. But it was so scary and had us all worried for some time!

Figure 20.5 *Micheal McGoldrick with his daughter. Our first pharmacist, Micheal was an APSO volunteer from Ireland.*

Micheal left us after two years and married his sweetheart Jane who had come out to visit him and to assist. She is also a pharmacist. On returning to Ireland they became the founders of Friends of Hospice Uganda in Ireland (FOHUI) and, together with Pauline Pierce, ran it for several years, being a conduit for Irish Aid funding and receiving donations from sponsored marathons, coffee mornings etc. They became Hospice Africa Ireland (HAI) in 2008. Micheal and Jane recently had their third child and have only just resigned from the Board of HAI. These two really committed people were among a long line of friends who supported FOHUI. Most of them were those who had an allegiance to Uganda and had been volunteers with APSO in Uganda and knew us. John O'Connor returned to Ireland with Margaret, his Ugandan wife and also gave leadership to the new association supported entirely by volunteers.

When APSO was dissolved in 2001, Irish Aid supported our volunteers through FOHUI, which had been formally registered in Ireland in 1999. Funding now comes directly from the Irish Government to Hospice Africa Ireland (HAI) as a grant. Irish Aid has helped us with several capital costs over the years, including the original house (now Merriman House) which they bought and renovated for us in 1994.

When our ambulance crashed in 1995 they gave us a grant for two used cars, one of which is still in use. They also contributed towards the completion of Kateregga House in 1997, which gave accommodation to those coming for training. They gave a major portion of funding for the educational clinical building, Rutembegwa House, in 2003. This included the Mary McAleese Lecture Theatre, opened by the Irish President in 2001. In 2005, Irish Aid secured the Distance Learning Diploma house. This was the house next door and opened up the compound into one site about half an acre in size.

Currently a new building is going up at Makindye – the Centre of Excellence for Clinical Palliative Care for Africa. It will include a clinical area, twice the area of the previous clinical building, administration and eventually, international programmes upstairs. It has been funded 75% by Irish Aid and 25% by KPMG Ireland.

Figure 20.6 *The Centre of Excellence site in 1993.*

Figure 20.7 *The new Clinical Centre of Excellence, funded from Ireland, 2010. Designed by volunteer architect, Triona Stack, Dublin.*

In 2006, Irish Aid supported a consultancy into internet provision within HAU. They had funded the upgrade of the IT systems to support the DLD students throughout Africa. At the moment they are the major donors towards the new clinical building, essential because of the increase of 'walk-in' patients over the last few years. This building commenced in September 2008 and is to be opened in June 2010. Much of the recent development of HAI and funding have come to us through the assistance, both personal and organisational, of Aidan Eames, present Chairman of HAI, who has supported us for many years.

It can be seen that the people of Ireland have invested greatly in palliative care and we are tremendously grateful for their contribution.

The Irish Hospice Foundation

My first encounter with the Irish Hospice Foundation was an article I read by Mary Redmond, their founder, in 1994. Her father had died of cancer and she had been very touched by the difference that palliative care had made to him. Mary, a lawyer, had seen that there was a gap in the coordination of palliative care in Ireland, and founded IHF. Each time I was in Ireland I made a point of looking them up. From time to time, when they were not completely struggling, small funding was given to us which really helped us in those early days. Also, through IHF, The Rose Project, founded by Mary Donohoe, contributed to us, by helping with training and specialist registrar support.

A more concrete relationship has begun in the last three years. I had visited and talked to many in the IHF but came to know the present CEO, Eugene Murray after he attended a talk I gave at the Irish Palliative Care Association in 2007. Eugene approached me to say that it had been suggested to him by a mutual colleague, Professor Kathy Foley, that he do a documentary on our work. After hearing me speak he thought it might be possible. Eugene was a TV producer in his former life.

Professor David Clark, of the Observatory in End of Life Care, from Lancaster University, where I was an Honorary Lecturer, was then doing collaborative consultancy work with Eugene so we had another connection.

In 2009, a short video was made by IHF, showing the Irish connection with HAU. Featuring contributions from volunteers Dr Stephen Higgins and Dr Siobhan Kennelly among others, it has been most useful in drawing attention to our work and its history. It is available on YouTube and the Irish website www.hospiceafrica.ie. We are planning further cooperation and IHF is presently supporting the publication of this book.

Jersey

Jersey Overseas Aid came from a little country with a small population but with a big heart. They support many projects overseas. In 1994, the First Secretary of the British High Commission, Michael Frost, introduced us to Anne Bailhache, then President of the Overseas Aid Commission in Jersey. Anne and her husband visited and stayed with us several times over the next few years and gave the initial support for Kateregga House and funding towards the pharmacy. The first pharmacy, housed in the kitchen in Merriman House, was then incorporated into the new clinical building.

Anne's daughter, a general practitioner in Jersey, later came to work with us for six months to learn how we had adapted palliative medicine to a resource-poor setting. She came because, having visited Ecuador in South America, she had realised that there was a great need for palliative care there and was committed to dedicating her life to bringing palliative care to that country. She contributed a lot to us during her six months with us and later settled down in Ecuador. Since then she has married an Ecuadorian dentist and they now have two children.

When we first met Jersey Overseas Aid they felt they needed a medical opinion of our work. They sent out a doctor consultant of their own to work with us for a few days. At the time we were offering pain and symptoms control for patients attending the clinic in Nsambya so we took him along to the clinic. At that clinic we were asked to see a patient who had been in severe pain for several weeks and constantly had to come back to the clinic for help. It is extremely difficult to find out the cause of abdominal pain in HIV patients. But we were able to give her morphine immediately and a week's supply. Pain was completely controlled and both the doctor from Jersey and those working in the clinic were completely astonished by the change in this lady. We had won over Jersey Overseas Aid, and more importantly the confidence of the HIV clinic team.

The Netherlands

Ria Van der Hel (now Ria Broekenhuizen) first came out to stay with us in 1997. She and her husband had been devoted to palliative care. Ria was in her second marriage and married to the husband of a patient she had nursed in her role as a palliative care nurse. Prins, her husband, had leukaemia when she married him and she knew that they would not have long together. They were so much in love and it was a joy to be with them. Prins joined us as our principal walker at our annual sponsored walk the year before he died. All felt we truly had a Prince Prins with us!

Ria has developed support for our poorer patients contributing to the Comfort Fund, and she and her friends have created a fund called the Prins Fund in memory of her husband. Ria continues to support us with her love and prayers and the funds she has from friends.

Joan Kelly, our Irish supporter, now married to a Dutchman Ronald Scheer, has begun Hospice Africa the Netherlands (HATN). They are supported by a group who came out two years ago with a netball team, to play with the Ugandans but also to support our patients and families, bringing out a bus to travel in and leaving it behind for us, together with reconditioned computers etc. The members of the team had collected all this funding before they left the Netherlands. Presently HATN is supporting a new building in Mbarara to be built on land donated through Archbishop Paul, from the Catholic Archdiocese of Mbarara.

We have two other donor organisations in the Netherlands: CORDAID, who have supported us over many years and another donor which prefers to remain anonymous.

Figure 20.8 *Mr and Mrs Scheer.*
Day 1 of married life.

Figure 20.9 *Archbishop Paul about to lead the 10ᵗʰ Anniversary walk for MHM accompanied by community volunteers.*

USA

Our first relationship with American donors was in 2003. I was invited by Dr Joe O'Neill to speak at the White House Conference Centre in Washington as a part of presentations to possible donors to the PEPFAR fund (President's Emergency Program for AIDS Relief). I was one of the few speakers actually working in Africa, whereas the other speakers did not work in Africa but were speaking from a donor point of view or after a short visit to an African palliative care service, boosted by information collected off the internet. The presentations were well received, and I was approached by email from organisations who wanted to put my name on their headed notepaper in order to attract funds. I was warned against this and did not accept because we did not understand the full agendas of these organisations.

The PEPFAR fund became a reality twelve months later and it was to go to 15 countries in Africa and two in the Caribbean: 15 billion dollars was to go towards palliative care. But what did PEPFAR do? They changed the definition of palliative care so that support organisations could receive the same funds. Support organisations were developed in Africa when it was realised that hospital beds were completely full with HIV patients. These support organisations were to provide support at the community level mainly with food, blankets, mosquito nets, and very simple medications. In Uganda the first support organisation was started from Kitovu Mission Hospital in Masaka in 1986, and eventually became a separate home care service now based in Masaka. They are now the only support organisation in Uganda that has successfully grafted palliative care so that patients can receive the time and medication needed during critical care at the end of life.

Figure 20.10 *Dr Judy Hills (right), who started Hospice Africa USA in 2006 and comes every year to work with the team at Hoima, is seen here with a patient during her volunteering.*

TASO, the most famous support organisation in Africa, founded by Noerine Kaleeba, as related earlier, has become world renowned as a success story as to how an indigenous organisation can support so many people. They have done a wonderful job but have not been able to support the patients in severe pain. Although we have trained many people from TASO, many returned back to their workplace expecting to see a large number of patients – impossible in palliative care which is time-intensive. Because American donors want reports of large numbers being covered, support organisations are often donor-driven to see more and more, which reduces quality of care.

At hospice we have been supported by PEPFAR through the last four years. They actually have given us up to 50% of our financial needs over this time. For this we are most grateful. However, there have been problems: the reporting back is required frequently and we are sometimes not up to speed. The stress of deadlines has caused patient care to suffer as people are taken from patient care to complete reports and attend meetings. As we have adapted, it has become easier as the teams have been trained to handle this. So overall we are grateful for this special training through USAID.

The funding coming from PEPFAR is for AIDS alone. Our initial mission was for the cancer patient and we took on AIDS as a humanitarian approach in 1994. This means that for 50–60% of our patients that have cancer alone, we have to seek funding elsewhere. When we consider that the expertise to treat AIDS has come from our experience with cancer, this seems a little unfair. A further problem is that USAID, who deliver the grant, have taken a great interest in organisational development within HAU. This is to be commended, but for this they have brought in experts from outside who do not necessarily have an understanding of the ethos of the new specialty of palliative care. It would be beneficial if they could come to hospice to spend time and learn about it.

Our relationship with donors in the USA was moved forward by the founding of HA(USA) by Dr Judith Hills, a palliative care specialist, and her husband Lynn Murrell in 1996. They had great difficulty finding an affordable lawyer to help them with the legal work for registration and came up with a novel idea. Lynn, a vet, found a lawyer with several pets and offered free veterinary services while the constitution was being written. Thus HA(USA) was registered that year in the state of Vermont.

21 The Man with the Key Has Gone

Patience is a virtue, possess it if you can,
Seldom found in woman,
Never found in man.
W. Howard Coop

THOSE WHO HAVE read the book by Dr Ian Clarke[42] about his experiences in Uganda will know what I am getting at by the title of this chapter. The concept that the customer comes first was very foreign to Uganda in 1993 and the attitude that the seller is always right is still very common in most areas of officialdom. In the early days when there were only three of us and I was the doctor, nurse, driver, advocate and accountant all in one, I spent many unpleasant hours waiting to see those I had made appointments with.

Many offices played a game called 'the run around'. You go to the office concerned and somebody is sitting behind a desk reading a paper. You tell them you've come to see so and so, and you're told to sit and wait. So very humbly you sit and wait and your friend continues to read the paper and not even pick up the telephone to indicate that you have arrived or even let you know if the person has arrived. You finally stand up because you have patients to see and say, 'I have been here twenty minutes.'

They tell you to wait.

After another twenty minutes you stand up again and let them have it. 'Don't you realise I have been waiting and I've come to help the very sick people of Uganda and I sit here and wait while you read the paper!'

Sometimes seeing a *m'zungu* lady going hysterical works but most of the time they say, 'Excuse me, you are at the wrong desk. Go to the next one.' The next desk say, 'Go down two floors.' Then they direct you back to the first guy with the newspaper. Then the guy with the newspaper is nearly finished and gives you his full attention and says, 'I thought you wanted to see – so and so – but the man you wanted to see thought you weren't here and has gone out. So let me make you an appointment for another day.'

I am not very good at holding in my feelings and at this point I explode. This happened to me once in the Ministry of Finance. A

---

[42] Ian Clarke, *The Man with the Key Has Gone*, New Wine Ministries, 2004.

gentleman came to my help for he had seen me at church in Christ the King and tried to cool me down.

The other thing that can trigger a meltdown is asking you to come in for a document and then they say, 'Sorry, we can't see you today, we've lost the documents. Please bring them in again.' Another nod to Ian's book *The Man with the Key Has Gone* or 'He Who Holds the Key to the Documents Has Gone.'

I was one of the lucky ones coming from Kampala but many people come from long distances and wait for hours only to find that the man with the key is gone. They have limited time and don't have the funds to stay the night but . . . who cares?

Demonstrating the pecking order

We are all VIPs but some are more important VIPs than others. In Uganda, and other African countries, there are several ways of demonstrating your level of importance. If you are invited to be the guest of honour at an occasion, the plebs are invited to come at least half an hour before. The programme is due to commence with your speech at 9 am. If you are important then you come half an hour late. If even more important an hour late and so on, until, if it is a member of parliament or the President, then they might come several hours late! This has held up proceedings on many occasions so now we just start with the programme and slot in the VIP when he arrives!

Others may not turn up at all and when you ask why, they had another more important engagement! That puts you in your place!

The challenges of working in a foreign country

I have lived in many countries, but Uganda has been my home for the longest of all the countries I have lived in. The people are so joyous and welcoming to all. They have provided me with a home, a family and supported me in my mission to bring this care to all in need. So when I write about some of the conflicts, I want you to remember that there are so many good things. I love Uganda.

This world is very interesting. Every country has a different history which has resulted in the way their different social systems have been created and moulded, and the different approach of their government, health systems, religions and basic tribalism. And when people are dying we need to be very aware of their beliefs and expectations which also differ from place to place.

One of the problems is that Westerners feel that they know it all. And too often they will come into a foreign country which has a different culture from anything they are used to or know about and yet they are filled with a superhuman confidence that their own experiences and ideas will create great benefits for that country. Often, this approach benefits nobody except for the CV of the person promoting their own concept of their specialty.

So on entering a new country it is important to understand that we are going to have to learn an awful lot. The learning process is continuous because changes in countries are very rapid these days and we need to be sensitive to the changes occurring around us in regard to our patients. This can only be done by sharing and listening to the people of the country.

Being Irish British made me more and more aware of the aggressive feelings towards the occupation by the British during the time of the Empire. For example, I found in 1981 that bureaucracy was rampant in India. But in England at that time, bureaucracy had changed dramatically and consulting was the order of the day. I had to learn this the hard way while I was travelling the whole of India to interview the elderly as part of my study of the Elderly of India for my dissertation for the Masters degree at the Liverpool School of Tropical Medicine. My travels were greatly hampered by the delays in getting that essential piece of paper which ensured your seat on the train at the right time, on the right day and in the right carriage.

There had to be a piece of paper held by the officer at the window to correspond with your own. Minutes and hours would be spent looking for it. If you didn't have it, then no matter what you received from the same office in exchange for your money, your booking would not be honoured. This piece of paper represented bureaucracy in that it had to be stamped by so many people before you could move on to the train then afterwards the copy was often lost by the time you reached your destination. Hence, I had to accept that I would have to sleep in the men's compartment of the train back to Benares (Varanasi) from Madras because they had lost (or sold to someone else) the copy of my ticket for the women's carriage.

Some of the Indians longed for the British colonial days but many were still very angry at the struggle they had in gaining independence. Even though it is now many years since many of the countries in the old British Empire received their independence, there is frequently overkill as these countries struggle to show that they are independent and capable of doing everything themselves. This is understandable and those of us working in these countries have to be humble enough to allow credit to be taken by the people of the country and not always seek it for ourselves.

The word is the name of the game

As you get older you realise that words that had a very definite meaning in your early life have changed. For example, there are now three ways to say that you're 'OK': 'cool' used to mean you were feeling cold, but now it means OK or acceptable; 'awesome' meant something that was truly mind-blowing but now just indicates 'It's OK' ('How's your tea?' 'Awesome'); 'I'm good' used to mean 'I'm a good person' but now it's just another way of saying 'I'm OK with this situation.'

So too in the hospice world and possibly in the health world, different things have different meanings. For example in hospitals a patient is somebody who is sick. The same patient, no matter their past or future, becomes a receiver from the health system. They lose all their character and even clothes if admitted into the hospital. What they have to contribute may not be heeded by the health professionals or their teams (including receptionists). The patient becomes an anonymous person. The definition of a patient in the dictionary is 'person receiving or registered to receive medical treatment'.[43]

When support care began with patients for HIV/AIDS in the North and transferred to the developing world PWLA (people living with AIDS) were very outspoken – they didn't want to be called 'patient' indicating that they were sick. So in their wisdom they decided to be called 'clients' by their caring organisations. This word indicates that there is some kind of business arrangement between the client and business. In the developed world, where HIV/AIDS patients are very vocal, after the first initial shock that they might die, having taken antiretrovirals (ARVs) many may become very outspoken and work

---

[43] Oxford Compact Dictionary

together in groups to challenge policies. This was often in line with the fact that most of the early sufferers of HIV were gay, and the gay communities were pushing for recognition and respect both from government, their friends and families.

I noted this around 1998 at a conference in UK, where we the speakers were often shouted down by action groups. This was repeated recently in the recent AIDS Congress in Mexico. Maybe the word 'client' is more liberating than the word 'patient', but in hospice care it does not denote that our patients are our guests and we are sharing hospitality. We share and we care for each other.

Some of our donors, who are prepared to give funding for HIV/AIDS only, indicate they want our patients to be called 'clients'. But the people we care for are physically sick. They are our patients and our guests but they are certainly not our clients. If I go to work on an assembly line for motor cars I am an employee or a member of staff. If I join hospice or a palliative care team I become a member of that team.

We work as a team and a family but we don't call each other brother and sister as they do in the churches. We refer to each other as a co-team member or a colleague. The use of such words helps us to remember our ethos and although salaries are important to maintain ourselves and families, we have the privilege of sharing in the joys and sorrows in a special time of life and this brings great personal joy.

Also our way of living and behaving is interpreted differently in different cultures. This is something that has to be learned as you move from country to country. Every culture has its own right to its understanding of behaviour. For example, in England it is OK for a boy and girl to hold hands, but not OK for a boy and boy to hold hands. In Uganda you will not see a boy and girl holding hands but you may see a boy and boy holding hands. This indicates that it is OK for males to show affection for each other in public but not towards a female.

These outward expressions of love between a man and woman, which we accept in the Western culture, are not acceptable in most African cultures. It's not only holding hands but going further, with kissing and hugging or looking into each other's eyes romantically, that is not allowed in the Ugandan culture. These things are for the bedroom and the bedroom is private. In the past, Uganda being very poor and being on the Equator, people worked for twelve hours of daylight and if there was nothing else to do they slept for twelve hours. There was very little entertainment until electricity, television and nightclubs livened things up. So using the words 'Let's go and play' meant 'Let's go play sex'. That was a game that could be carried out in the dark.

Working in hospice we have to be very aware of what is acceptable and what is not within the culture. We are welcomed into homes rich and poor. There is no rush around to tidy up the house as there would be in the West. These people are open and friendly and willing to share their joys and sorrows at this special time for the patient. However, a few times I have had to receive messages from friendly nurses not to go that direction in conversations I would be having. There are areas that are taboo for a woman to enter into in conversation and some areas where a family is not prepared to go. I have to say I am not always in agreement and if speaking in English would pursue it if it was important for the well-being of the patient.

A dress code is also important and hot pants, miniskirt and spaghetti-strapped tanktops are out. Very arrogant men have been known to strip a local girl in scanty attire in public.

Sometimes our behaviour and language are misunderstood. To certain tribes in Uganda to raise your voice is to insult them. The Ugandan tends to be very calm in public although they can lose their tempers badly, especially the man who is never prepared to admit that he has been wrong. That would mean losing face.

One day in a murram back road in Kampala, a taxi driver pulled out a chain threatening to beat me after I expressed my anger towards him for pulling out in front of me without signalling. In Uganda the matatu man rules on the road – or so he thinks!

In our local tribe, the Buganda, little girls are made to kneel down to their brother regardless of the relevant age. This was a big shock to me when I went around with Henry Mary in the early days. Women and girls would go down to their knees in front of him. I was disgusted because in my book, people should only go down on their knees to God. Although this custom is practised in the villages, amongst the upper classes it is not quite so obvious. I have even had children doing this to me – little boys as well as little girls – as a sign of respect, but because of my upbringing I find this sad and always ask them not to do it.

This custom allows boys to think they are much better than girls and they will be allowed to beat them or treat them badly anyway. Corporal punishment is still frequent, despite the laws passed ten years ago prohibiting it in schools. Children are brought up with the idea that you can beat anything smaller than yourself and this leads to problems, particularly between boys and girls and older children. Bullying in schools has become acceptable.

Another day, driving back home from hospice, I heard sobbing behind a school. Then I saw twelve girls in their early teens lined up and a man in his early twenties beating them. I called one of the girls over to the fence to tell the man to come talk to me. He was very rude to me. I said I would write to the authorities. I could not understand why this man was left in charge. I wrote a letter and received a response of gratitude from the head teacher. I understand that he was dismissed. But the class of girls should never have been left with such an immature teacher.

I have also witnessed on many occasions people beating animals because animals are considered to be brainless. I once found two children beating a mother goat who had two little babies. When I stopped the car to tell them it was wrong and would they like me to beat them like that, they responded that she was troubling them! One of the problems I find very hard to understand is that many seem to think they can treat animals very badly.

Mbarara is the land of milk and honey and to go to one of the farms and see the cows in the fields, happily eating their grass, is a joy. These cows have quite a good life. But when the time comes for them to be slaughtered, if you could only see how they are transported! The Ancholi cows have huge horns as wide as six feet across. Getting into such a lorry with these horns creates a mess. They are left with their necks practically broken, legs sticking out all over the place. Not a sound from these animals as they are stunned. They are carried like this 300 km on horrible roads. There is talk about a Society for the Prevention of Cruelty to Animals but they are not visible enough. Small farmers will carry a huge pig on the back of a motor bike trussed up . . . I suppose I'm just a silly old *m'zungu* who cares for animals, but sometimes it's painful to see.

But then are humans treated better? People go to funerals packed on the back of wagons. The coffin may be on the bottom with people sitting on the coffin. Children and adults are all crammed into these wagons and once in a while there are these horrible road accidents where everyone dies. This happened to my gardener where everybody was killed but him. I have heard it said that there are more people killed on the road in Uganda in a month than all the plane crashes in the world every year. It hits the headlines for twenty-four hours and then people forget about it, but it leaves the families devastated.

Death in a young person in Africa can be a real tragedy. Very often the family has invested all they have in the education of this young boy, who would then look after the rest of the family. So if he dies it is the death not only of a loved one, but of the hopes and dreams for the salvation of the family.

Games people play

I have found that in the many cultures I have worked in, there are very few men that can accept being challenged by a woman. The woman may not realise that she is challenging them, but the fact that she is a woman adds greatly to the challenging element, in societies where everything has to appear to be coming from a man. Although of course we all know that behind every good man is a better woman!

In Uganda, for example, breaking bad news is not part of the culture. In its simplest form this comes down to the following: you are lost on a road so you stop and ask for some directions. This guy does not know the directions but he doesn't want to break the bad news so he makes an educated guess, which is usually wrong. Giving false news may be related to not wanting to lose face. Losing face, as I learned early on in Nigeria, is one of the worst things that could happen. This is so throughout the world of course, but it's a very big deal to African men.

Throughout the history of Hospice Uganda I have become very sensitive to the way people speak to me. I can tell when they are with us on the palliative care trail and I can tell when they are cooling off. But nobody tells you why they are cooling off and it may take many months or years till you find out the reason.

An example is when I first came and sought permission from the Ministry of Health to get morphine. Unknown to me, I offended many people. There were many different reasons for this. Possibly they believed morphine was trying to kill people or we would be creating a problem of addiction. But nobody approached me with their reasons. So I faced obstructions in many offices in the Ministry of Health at the time.

It would make life much simpler if they would openly talk about these reservations. We would call this having another agenda. But to a newcomer in Uganda it is a puzzle and can be very distressing as it is an obstacle to the real work – help for their brothers and sisters, our patients.

These kinds of reactions continue even today and I find it very hard when certain items have been deliberately kept from me. For example, it could be that a member of the team is being used by another organisation and is trying to serve two masters. Yet this could have been settled amicably with a sharing mentality between both employers.

Breaking bad news and passing the buck

The people not revealing the truth are usually involved in trying to placate many others. Breaking bad news is a function of medical professionals. Yet doctors who refer patients to our team have often not been honest with their patient. Of course the patient, being aware that the doctor is not telling the truth, does not demand it as he or she is in a supplicant position most of the time, and their treatment relies on their being subject to the doctor or health worker.

The majority of our patients, when they come to us, tell us they have not been told of their diagnosis. This is sometimes untrue as the patient may be going through denial. But the news is not reinforced. Many patients go from doctor to doctor, accepting expensive treatment and hoping for a cure. So by the time they see us they are broke as well as broken and trying to grasp reality. This can be compared to the woman in St Mark's Gospel:

> There was a woman who had suffered terribly ... for twelve years even though she had been treated by many doctors. She had spent all her money, instead of getting better she got worse all the time.
> Mark 5:25.26

There are other delaying tactics of course. The traditional healer, who promises cure and prescribes herbs endlessly, is trusted implicitly. The new 'Born Again' or 'Savedy' churches promise that if the patient goes to their church and trusts enough in God they will not need medical treatment – and if they are on it they should stop. Yes, it does happen in Uganda and many other African countries.

In one of our early training programmes in dealing with breaking bad news, during the role play we had a doctor playing a doctor and the nurse playing the mother of a child who had been diagnosed with cancer. The mother of the child was asking the doctor questions about the diagnosis and after a few minutes, as the message was sinking in, she asked, 'Is my child going to die?' to which the reply was: 'I'm going to refer you to a counsellor.'

This indicated to us how absolutely *not* prepared are our doctors to break bad news. This is the doctor's role, and one of the most precious times he will have to support a patient, and he must be ready to give this news. Occasionally he can delegate it to a nurse in the team but he must not refer this to a faceless counsellor, unless he/she has a face, is a member of the team and is fully informed of the patient's problems and the medical reasons for the bad prognosis.

Passing the buck is not acceptable in matters of life and death and shows little feelings for the patient and relatives. Sheila Cassidy[44] writes eloquently on this as well as illustrating it, describing that at this point the patient is completely naked (Figures 21.2 and 21.3). The doctor must strip him/herself of all in order to discuss prognosis, and having considered his/her own death, is now at the same level of helplessness as the patient. In other words, our role may be just holding hands, giving the news and being humble enough to admit we do not have all the answers.

Figure 21.1   *Singapore conference in Palliative Care 1988. Left to right:
Dr Sheila Cassidy (UK), Dr Cynthia Goh (Singapore) and
Dr Fumikazu Takeda from Japan.*

---

[44] Sheila Cassidy, *Sharing the Darkness: The Spirituality of Caring,* Darton, Longman & Todd, 1988.

The role of counselling in palliative care

So what is a counsellor and what is their role in palliative care? Let me give you a hysterical historical background of counsellors in Uganda. Traditionally there is a role for a counsellor in the tribal systems of Uganda. The counsellor in the tribe will be appointed according to what the counselling is about.

For example when a young girl is getting married she will be counselled by the *senga*. This is usually an auntie who will instruct the girl in the facts of life and how to be a good wife within the tribal tradition (which in reality means bowing and scraping to the men); also if there is a problem between a husband and wife before they seek a divorce there will be an attempt at reconciliation with the tribal counsellors.

However the work of counsellors in HIV and bereavement came in from the West because the West, in their wisdom, had decided that people with HIV need much more than medical care. And of course HIV did in the West, where initially young men were dying very quickly from this new disease. So counsellors were imported to Uganda, to train Ugandan counsellors. After a short period of training, they were highly marketable for support organisations, because in order to impress donors from Western organisations, they needed to have counsellors. Their salaries were higher than that of nurses, so many nurses who needed more money were now being trained as counsellors and leaving the profession.

Of course nurses made much better counsellors with their background and were snapped up for training. Now we are in the situation where counsellors come to counsel people in severe pain, and can do nothing because there are not enough nurses to control the pain. Even one of our own nurses, although she had signed an agreement that she would stay with hospice for two years after training, moved to be a counsellor after finishing a nine-month training programme, which was such a waste.

After counsellors were entrenched into the system an English gentleman came out as a volunteer with a grant for £100,000 to help the counsellors cope with stress. He then had to explain what stress meant to most of them and started taking them off for weekend retreats to relieve the stress that they did not know they had! Of course they were delighted – a weekend away with expenses paid, who wouldn't be?

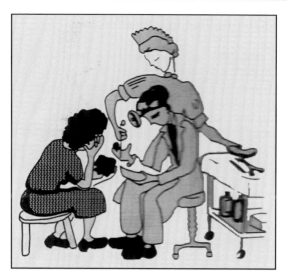

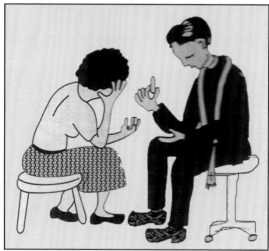

Figure 21.2 Above: *The doctor, armed with his competence and his instruments and protected by his aide.* **Below:** *A priest performing his sacramental ministry. Here we see him wearing his stole and clerical collar protected by having a role to play and a ritual to perform. From Sheila Cassidy,* Sharing the Darkness: The Spirituality of Caring, *Darton, Longman & Todd, 1988, Figures 6.1 and 6.2, p. 179. Reproduced by kind permission of the author and publisher.*

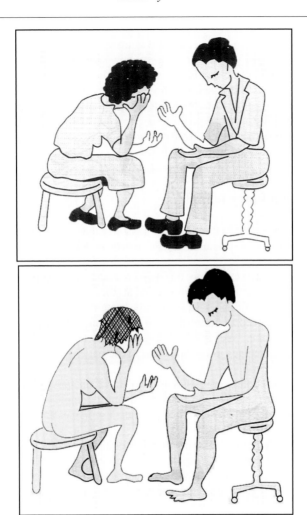

Figure 21.3 Above*: A patient meeting with either doctor or clergyman when he has exhausted the physical aspects of his ministry. He is left with his hands empty, but with his resources of counselling still available.* **Below:** *Both patient and carer stripped of their resources, present to each other, naked and empty-handed, as two human beings. From Sheila Cassidy,* Sharing the Darkness: The Spirituality of Caring, *Darton, Longman & Todd, 1988, Figures 6.3 and 6.4, p. 180. Reproduced by kind permission of the author and publisher.*

So when the evaluation came, and I was invited to the presentation, I had the nerve to ask the counsellors present, how many knew what stress was before this volunteer came to the country. They all responded honestly that in fact they didn't know. This is just giving an example of how Western culture can lead to the waste of essential money for patient care in the developing world. We find that the counsellors are not trained to deal with people who are critically ill or dying. Hence hospice now has a course for counselling in end-of-life care.

Multidisciplinary team?

Yes, the hospice team is multidisciplinary in other countries. But I have yet to be convinced, because when a patient is dying, he or she usually wants to share with only one person, and this is usually the nurse. The family gets very attached to this person and shares their sorrow and struggles. Bringing in another person at this point is not acceptable because many confidences have already been shared with the palliative care nurse. We need to be sensitive to the feelings of our patients at this very special time. We in the team need to take responsibility for explaining the changes in the body and in the patient's behaviour as they come towards death.

Also, the health professionals who make up the multidisciplinary team abroad are usually not available in most remote areas where the poor are in need of palliative care. We must use nurses and volunteers to provide all for our patients.

Thus the role of the occupational therapist, physiotherapist, social worker or even pastor at Hospice Africa Uganda may be more to train our nurses to be able to meet the eventualities of their disciplines, using local culture and facilities, rather than providing this themselves.

22 The Story of Affordable Opioids in Africa

Oral opioids have opened the gate for holistic palliative care in Africa.
Anne Merriman

THE KEY ADVANCE that has helped us move so quickly in Africa since 1990 has been the availability of affordable oral morphine. This began the control of severe pain for cancer and allowed those who suffered such pain to be able to be treated in their own home, accept holistic care, and to plan for their families and themselves. It allowed them to come to peace with their God.

The two countries that had palliative care before 1990 were Zimbabwe (1979) and South Africa (1980). At the time of the founding of these hospices there was a large and fairly dominant white population and the initial hospices were geared towards the needs of the white populations. Morphine was affordable in the expensive forms that we find in the affluent West, i.e. tablets, injections for pumps etc.

Figure 22.1 *Peter Mikajo makes up oral morphine in the pharmacy at hospice.*

223

My first experience of making oral morphine from powder was in Singapore. When we started the first home care service there, oral morphine was not widely available. The very helpful pharmacist in the National University Hospital found a formula for oral morphine which was very cheap. We were the first people to bring pain control into the homes of Singapore. Patients who were not responding to chemotherapy or radiotherapy at that time were sent home, often without adequate control of pain or symptoms, and were expected to return to outpatient clinics for follow-up. Thus the first home care service for palliative care was commenced there in 1985.

Once oral morphine was available, the amount of morphine used in the country has greatly increased over the years.

Thus, the combination of government support, available oral morphine, the essential medications for pain and symptom control and the training of health workers led by a person with 'fire in the belly', will provide the ingredients for developing a service, education programmes and reaching those in need throughout the country. But we are not there yet by any means!

Kenya

When I first visited Nairobi with a view to becoming the first Medical Director of Nairobi Hospice, then in an infant state, I insisted, as I have outlined earlier, that I could not come unless affordable oral morphine was available to the patients. I witnessed some terrible suffering among the patients in 1989. I was notified a few months later that Professor Kasili, Chair of the Board of Nairobi Hospice, had negotiated with the Ministry of Health to import morphine powder. Oral morphine was to be made in Nairobi Hospital (a private hospital) under the supervision of a lady pharmacist who was also on the Hospice Board. This really made a great difference to our patients and families and was extended to the rest of Kenya following our education programmes, but in fact the oral solution of morphine was produced only in Nairobi Hospital pharmacy for many years.

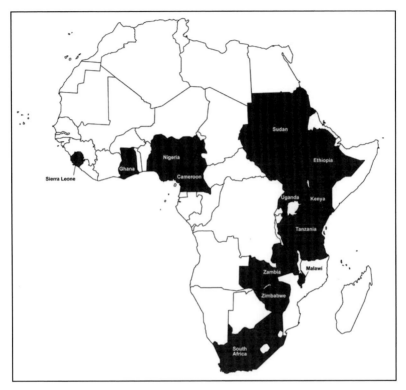

Figure 22.2 *Map of countries in Africa with affordable oral morphine for use in the home, May 2010. Courtesy of Anthony Greenwood of the Observatory in End of Life Care (OELC) at Lancaster University.*

Moving into African countries in the 21st century

Before visiting an African country with advocacy, we research the logistics, the services in place and the need for initiation or expansion so that we are working with those already on the ground. We need the country to invite us and to have key person in place to bring us to the necessary government and health officials, the hospitals, the appropriate schools of health education including the universities.

As part of the third objective of Hospice Africa, Dr Jagwe, our Senior Advisor in National Policy and I made nine visits to a number of countries in Africa (Tanzania, Malawi, Ethiopia, Zambia, Nigeria, Cameroon, Sierra Leone, and most recently Rwanda and Sudan), visiting the Ministry of Health, pharmacists and the training schools and universities for palliative care. This was part of our advocacy programme according to our Founding Mission, to avail affordable and culturally acceptable palliative care to all in need in Africa.

This advocacy is to sensitise governments re the need for introducing palliative care into the health policies and care for those suffering particularly from cancer and/or HIV/AIDS but which can be adapted to any other terminal illness. Our usual approach has been to meet with those who are responsible for health in government, medical and nursing schools and other health training institutions and in particular those who are responsible for ensuring the importation of the medications required to control pain and symptoms, and their distribution throughout the country.

Palliative care has been advocated for Africa and the world by WHO since 1986 but has only started moving throughout Africa since 2000. Up to then it was established in three countries only. The palliative care experts taking PC to other African countries have come from mainly from Uganda where palliative care has been accepted into the five-year Health Sector Strategic Plan, and the revised National Strategic Framework for HIV/AIDS since 2000. The statute, which allows midwives to prescribe pethidine for women in labour delivered in their homes, was changed in 2002 to include nurses and clinical officers with specialist training at HAU, allowing them to prescribe morphine for the suffering. Uganda is still the only country in the world where prescribers have been increased under law to meet the needs of millions suffering from pain. This is a model that can be copied by other African countries who have diminishing available doctors, presently the only health workers in most countries allowed to prescribe class A drugs.

The palliative care need in Africa

The map in Figure 22.3 indicates the situation of palliative care in Africa in 2006. There has been little improvement since. Uganda is seen as a model for palliative care but we are still not even reaching 10% of those in need in Uganda through our own service or through those we are training.

The figures in Table 22.1 do not include those dying of renal failure, cardiac failure, diabetes and neurological conditions etc. It can be seen that the populations in need are huge yet those trained to deal with these situations are still a drop in the ocean.

Table 22.1 Estimates from population, prevalence of cancer and prevalence of AIDS patients in need of palliative care based on prevalence of HIV.[45]

HDI[a] No.	Country	Population (millions)	Cancer in need of PC (000s)	AIDS in need of PC (000s)	Total in need of PC (000s)
150	Sudan	41	123	32	155
154	Uganda	32	96	171	267
158	Nigeria	148	444	430	874
164	Malawi	14	5.5	165	170.5
167	Rwanda	10.5	31.5	15	46.5
176	Congo	62	186	370	556
180	Sierra Leone	5.4	1.5	8.5	10

a. Human Development Index

Patients with illnesses such as HIV/AIDS and cancer experience considerable suffering and have a high symptom burden (even those on ARVs). Palliative care improves the quality of life of these patients. AIDS-related illness and cancers in Africa usually present late and there are indications that AIDS is reducing but cancer is on the increase. Even with the advent of ARVs in some areas, diagnosis and curative treatment for cancers are still largely inaccessible to the majority. In Uganda less than 5% of all cancers present for radio-oncology and the majority present too late for curative therapy. About 57% of the population still have not seen a health worker in their lives and they too are lying in pain awaiting death in the villages. Yet relief is possible using simple, affordable, appropriate, palliative care, provided health workers can be trained.

---

[45] Anne Merriman, January 2010, sourced from Human Development Index, UNDP, 2009 and CIA Country Fact Book.

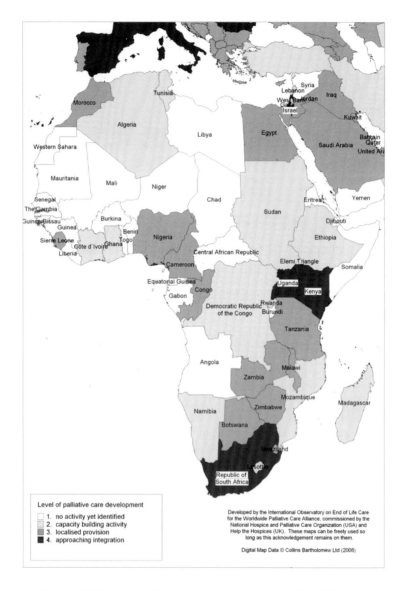

Figure 22.3 *Level of palliative care development in Africa, 2006.*

The feasibility study countries and beyond

During the feasibility study for Hospice Africa in 1993 described more fully in Chapter 7, the three countries that were strongly considered were Kenya (Moi University), Nigeria and Uganda. Kenya already had morphine and we visited the Ministry of Health in Uganda and Nigeria. Both agreed to import the morphine. Once we had settled on Uganda, morphine was imported. Nigeria was to delay the importation of oral morphine up until 2006 when this was negotiated by Professor Olaiten Soyannwo, the founder of the Centre for Palliative Care in Nigeria (CPCN), the hospice centre attached to UCH Ibadan.

Advocacy to other countries commenced seriously in the year 2000. Dr Jagwe and I moved to six countries in the next three years, bringing advocacy to the governments and to the undergraduate schools, universities and health institutions. Our reports are available for Malawi, Zambia, Ethiopia, Nigeria and Cameroon. Today, all have accepted and are using affordable oral morphine for patients with severe pain. Ethiopia was the most recent to import morphine powder (2009) but it has been delayed reaching the patients, while they research a longer shelf life at their own laboratories at ePharm, Addis Ababa.

Malawi

Looking at the countries we approached, you can see there was a trend. For example Malawi has moved faster than the other countries in spreading palliative care. And yet Malawi was the poorest of the countries. They had started palliative care at Lighthouse in Lilongwe. This is an AIDS support organisation, which has received a lot of international support and sees many patients and families. It is a similar model to the Mildmay Centre in Uganda. However, they were only providing support care up to 2001 because the team had no training in the model essential for pain and symptom control.

After our visit to Malawi, Lamek Tambo, the nurse coordinator of the palliative section, came to Uganda and worked with hospice for a month. He later obtained a Diploma in Palliative Care from Nairobi Hospice and Oxford Brookes University. Once morphine powder was imported into the country, Lighthouse became the centre where it was made into solutions and distributed to other organisations. Meanwhile the application to the Global Fund included morphine tablets and not the solution. The tablets are approximately twenty times more expensive per mg. However tablets were imported, funded by the Global Fund. But economically this meant less funding to support the patients in Malawi, most of whom were under the poverty line and could not even afford food.

Lucy Finch is a Malawian nurse who volunteered with HAU in Kampala for five years while her husband, Tony, was stationed here with the Forestry Commission. After Tony retired they planned to move back to Malawi. But Lucy had seen what could be done and shortly after arriving she commenced palliative care from her home in Salima in 2003. This became Ndi Moyo, a free-standing hospice in Salima, two years later. She says of herself in her first report:

> I am a Malawian who for the last 38 years has lived outside of Malawi. I came back to Malawi in April 2002 where I want to retire but also to volunteer my services.
>
> I am a nurse by profession. Like so many Malawians, I have had close relatives dying of AIDS and experienced the suffering that they go through. I have also, through my volunteer work with Hospice Uganda from 1997 to 2002, experienced that this suffering could be largely eliminated through palliative care. I have for the last two years volunteered as a nurse[46] for SASO and one and a half years at Lilongwe Catholic Diocese HBC Programme, Salima Parish and here encountered the great suffering that the chronically ill clients are experiencing in this area as well.
>
> Because of my special interest and experience with palliative care I find that this is where I best can contribute in the fight against HIV/AIDS, at the same time giving other chronically ill clients like those suffering from cancer a more dignified death, and overall to make Malawi a more humane society.

Today, Ndi Moyo is the only free-standing hospice in Malawi, a beacon of light and hope, promoting the ethos and spirit of hospice and palliative care. They are based on the Hospice Uganda model and have no inpatients. Their care for patients is totally within the home or in hospital.

---

[46] Professional details about Lucy Finch: Registered General Nurse (UK), Certified Midwife. Affiliations with Carer and Nurse for Salima Catholic Parish HBC Initiative and SASO. Advisor and board member to Baptist Clinic. Expertise: 20 years' nursing in UK and Zambia, five years as a volunteer nurse with Hospice Africa Uganda.

Figure 22.4 *Lucy Finch (wearing Hospice T-shirt) on a home visit in 2004.*

Following a visit and assessment by Dr and Mrs Phipps from Hospice Africa (UK) in 2004, HA was approached for support for a children's programme (Umodzi) from QEUCH (Queen Elizabeth

University College Hospital in Blantyre). Later, HA was also approached to support the adult palliative care section in the Department of Medicine (Tiyanjane Clinic) at the same hospital. The palliative care team at the Presbyterian Mission Hospital in Mulanje was supported the following year. We also supported the Palliative Care Association of Malawi (PCAM) from 2004. This is now supported by USAID through APCA.

When Dr Jagwe and I, together with Anne Lloyd-Williams from the Diana Fund, revisited Malawi two years after the importation of oral morphine in 2004, we were absolutely amazed at the number of organisations that had begun palliative care. Five such organisations came to the university to present to us. Three had access to morphine and the others were on track to receive it that year. This was one of my most encouraging experiences in Africa.

Looking at Malawi today with its great progress in palliative care and the eagerness of the new teams to care for each other and their patients, we have been tempted from time to time to think that we should put a model in Malawi and leave Uganda. But each country will have its own model and leaving Uganda when things get bigger and more difficult is a copout. Malawi will be a model in its own way and we will assist them all we can as a part of our initial mission for helping all of Africa. Uganda is the present model and has built standards, and working with those at heart, we can support each other to continue.

Zambia

If we compare Malawi with its neighbouring country Zambia, we wonder what the ingredients are that make things move in palliative care. Zambia's first efforts at modern palliative care started with Catholic Sisters from Ireland. One Sister had visited me while I was in Nairobi Hospice, Sister Crucis. She had subsequently received funds from Irish Aid to build Our Lady's Hospice in Lusaka.

Meanwhile Zambia had a long history of Polish nuns and priests. They had been there many years and had been running orphanages since the 1940s. The Polish Sisters had two 'hospices' developed to meet the needs of the AIDS epidemic, but up to then without analgesics for severe pain. One of their hospices that we visited in Lusaka was dealing with HIV/AIDS from diagnosis onwards. They had a school on the compound to cater for children affected by HIV/AIDS. Actually palliative care was a minimal part of their work. However, they came with the concept of

Polish Palliative Care and actually Shalunga Cromwell, who was employed by them, was sent to Poland to learn about palliative care. Cromwell was on our first programme for the Distance Learning Diploma. At the time of our visit in 2004, Cromwell had left the Polish Hospice and was working for a palliative care organisation, Cara Counselling Center, contributing to the support work.

Figure 22.5 *Orphans being cared for by the Sisters in Zambia.*

On the initial visit Shalunga Cromwell arranged for us to meet the people concerned with providing palliative care and to visit the government pharmacist and the National Teaching Hospital. This is one of the only countries that had actually imported powdered morphine. But its use was limited to the cancer patients in the hospital. It was made up using the obsolete formulas previously known as Brompton's cocktail, mist euphoria etc. Patients were not allowed to use it in the home.

The chief pharmacist at the hospital was an uncle of Cromwell and promised that they would negotiate with the government to have more morphine powder imported. They also promised to change the policy that it could only be available to cancer patients so that it could also be used in the homes for both cancer and HIV patients. But this did not happen. Today the policies in Zambia are changing a little faster. APCA has taken over the advocacy there.

We also visited the undergraduate schools of medicine and clinical officers who were both enthusiastic to bring palliative care into the curriculum.

The biggest problem we found in Zambia was that organisations professing to give palliative care were not working together and there were many conflicting divisions which basically were due to oneupmanship. This made advocacy with a united front impossible. There was no unity in training or setting up programmes and a lot of rivalry existed. After this visit and reporting back, nothing was carried forward. The rivalry amongst the organisations caused Cromwell to leave and he went to a private organisation. Hence there was nobody left with fire in their belly to carry it through.

The conclusion was that the palliative care in Zambia was mainly support care and will remain so until morphine solution is made available for use in the hospices, and those delivering it are trained in its use and in palliative care.

With the development of the African Palliative Care Association (APCA), several visits have been made, creating a palliative care association in Zambia. Pure oral morphine is now available but has a long way to go before it will be available throughout this country.

Ethiopia

Although every country is unique, Ethiopia is very different to other countries in East and Central Africa. Every country that we see today has been formed by its political past and its history of war. Ethiopia has had a very difficult time in the last 30–50 years. The country had for centuries been divided into two – Shoa, which goes back to the Queen of Sheba who had a child with the King of Ethiopia – and the rest of the country. The people of Shoa consider themselves direct descendants of the Queen of Sheba and are very proud of their heritage. The royal family headed the country and Emperor Haile Selassie had very high status and was both autocratic and bureaucratic. Education and moving forward had been confined to the peoples of Shoa for generations. The rest of the country remained within their traditional tribal systems and due to poverty few went to school. They were subsistence farmers and shepherds.

In 1975 when I first visited Ethiopia on behalf of another NGO based in Liverpool, there had been a revolution similar to that in Russia where the people turned against the royal family. Emperor Haile Selassie was in prison and the government had decided to bring in communism from China. The country was teeming with Chinese teaching the Little Red Book of Chairman Mao in the universities. The students from the universities and the colleges, who had been trained in the Little Red Book, were then sent out to teach the whole country the elements of Chinese Communism. While I was still in the country, Haile Selassie died under suspicious circumstances in prison,[47] and members of the royal family were killed or just disappeared.

Although it was a known and declared communist government, people were under the dictatorship of Haile Mariam. Anybody who performed out of line either had to leave the country or disappeared. Meanwhile Ethiopia was at war with Eritrea, its neighbour. The Eritreans had received a lot of education and progress had been made. Eritrea also owned the ports.

Because the countries were at war, boys and girls were recruited into the army at very young ages. In 1981, this was to be brought to reality as two of these children came to my home in Liverpool at the request of their father, a doctor who was a fellow student with me on the Masters Programme in International Community Health at the Liverpool School of Tropical Medicine. Asmerom, who was Eritrean by birth, was married to Belletu, an Ethiopian lady, distantly related to the royal family. His daughter, Frehiwot, was 16 and was about to be recruited into the army.

I agreed for Frehiwot to stay in Liverpool and she completed her education there with the help of Margaret Kemp, the mother of the only other girl in her class, who took Frey to her home while I was in Singapore. Frey then went to Ireland where she completed her nursing training at the MMM Foundations hospital, then the International Missionary Training Hospital in Drogheda. She has now settled down married to an Irishman and has two lovely children. She is working in the

---

[47] Although circumstances surrounding Haile Selassie's death remain unresolved, his followers believe he was murdered. 'He was killed brutally because he was a good man, as all good men are killed,' said the head priest celebrating the Mass at his official funeral.

Blackrock Clinic in Dublin for many years now. She also supports our work in Ethiopia when she can.

Figure 22.6 *Frehiwot, aged 17, my Ethiopian daughter, in Liverpool.*

Her little brother, Henock aged 11, could not speak any English and went to a Liverpool school for a few months and ended up with a Liverpool accent! He returned to Ethiopia with his father at the end of the academic year, but returned later to complete his education in IT in London. He has now settled in New York and is married to an Ethiopian lady. Sadly Dr Asmerom died in 1994 and his widow Belletu commutes between her children and Ethiopia.

I visited Ethiopia several times before the set-up of Hospice Uganda. By the time we visited in 2003, the ex-President, Haile Mariam, was in exile living in Zambia but the government that had taken over was extremely bureaucratic. People still lived in fear. Poverty was rife, HIV/AIDS was spreading very quickly because of the army and economic situation. Young women who were stuck in poverty were rapidly taken up in prostitution and many were dying leaving behind orphans. Even the support groups were short on basic medications and had been warned by the government that they were using too much.

This was the first country that I had been to where you could actually feel the depression among the people and even the missionaries who were trying to make a move in humanitarian work. Dr Jagwe and I visited the Ministry of Health training schools. Strangely they agreed with everything we said and they were excited to start. But three months later nothing had happened. When we went back with Cecilia Sepulveda, Head of the Department of Cancer and Palliative Care at WHO Geneva, we again presented the advocacy tools, the figures of those in need. We were told definitely that the morphine would be brought in. But again nothing happened until late in 2008, when powdered morphine was imported for the first time.

Meanwhile two Ethiopian nurses had been accepted into our Distance Learning Programme. One of them worked in Black Lion Hospital and the other worked with an NGO. It was very difficult for them to learn because the language in Ethiopia is Amharic. This is the language for teaching and all communication in the ministries. Not only is it a difficult language but it has a completely different alphabet. Both of our Ethiopian students took longer to complete the Distance Learning Diploma, because of this problem. Having visited Black Lion Hospital, we realised the suffering of the patients they were caring for. Over the years since then, several American groups have moved in, claiming to carry palliative care with them. But recent reports indicate there is very little happening on the ground and very few patients are being helped.

One of the biggest problems for expats trying to work in Ethiopia is the difficulty obtaining visas. One palliative care doctor from the UK, who went in with her husband who was employed to work in a university, attempted to start some form of palliative care scheme. Husband and wife spent six months there, during which none of their papers was processed, and then they spent several months trying to leave! This did not encourage others coming to assist and there certainly were reasons to feel hopeless.

Recently, however Hospice Ethiopia has been founded by Tsigereda, who was one of the nurses who completed the Diploma with us. She later came with a colleague to attend our programme for initiators

in Africa. This was followed by a visit to Ethiopia by Catherine
Nawangi, Dr Jane Graham and me. Things are improving and there is a
real feeling that palliative care might move ahead, now that morphine
powder is in the country.

Figure 22.7 *Sister Tsigereda (left) with Catherine Nawangi (right) on a home
visit in Addis, 2009.*

Since then several donors and Professor Dan Hinshaw from Ann
Arbor University in Michigan have visited and there is great hope for
support from the International Orthodox Churches to assist the work for
patients through the small service commenced by Tsigereda.

USAID is funding two projects through two US universities to
bring palliative care to AIDS patients. These are mainly aiming to
provide education and research but all this needs to be based on a clinical
service. Hospice Ethiopia is providing the only clinical service in the
homes but is restricted for lack of funds.

Nigeria

Our recent visits to Nigeria have been mainly to Ibadan where Professor Olaiten Soyannwo, Professor of Anaesthesiology, had conceived the idea of a hospice and palliative care centre attached to UCH Ibadan. However we are still in touch with Mrs Sola Fatumnbi, discussed in the feasibility study of 1993. She, like us all, is getting older, but attends any meetings in palliative care. She has also been looking after many patients referred back to Lagos from abroad over these years.

Figure 22.8 *Mrs Sola Fatumnbi of Lagos. Pioneer in Nigeria.*

Figure 22.9 *Professor Olaiten Soyannwo, the heart of the hospice at UCH Ibadan.*

These patients are referred to her from the countries where they have received treatments for their cancer and they are given a supply of morphine for their use on their return. They are returning to Nigeria to die at home with their families.

Nigeria has a population of 150 million and growing! The capital is now Abuja. This was a new capital formed twenty years ago to take over from Lagos. Lagos is a port and possibly the most populated city in Africa, renowned for traffic jams and for being unsafe. Much of the country's business is carried out there. Abuja is centrally placed in the country; it is so expensive to live in that most of those working there have to commute. The country is divided into six geopolitical zones, each big enough to be a country of its own. Abuja was selected for its central position so that each geo political zone could reach it.

Ibadan is about two hours' drive from Lagos, which still has the main international airport. The University of Ibadan was the first to have a medical school in Nigeria. This was established mainly by the British and they had very excellent teachers in the 1950s and '60s. Graduates were welcomed anywhere in the world and even today you will find many graduates of UCH in senior posts abroad. UCH Ibadan like many great universities in Africa deteriorated during the troubles which commenced with the Biafran War in 1966.

Twice when I visited UCH Ibadan, the wards were empty because the medical staff were on strike. Although Nigeria is thought to be oil-rich, most of the oil money has gone to the owners of the companies or directly to the government and directly from the government into the Swiss bank accounts of the leaders. Thus the oil wealth has not really helped the man in the street and there is constant unrest where the main oil rigs are.

Within the health services there are huge gaps between doctors and nurses. There is a pecking order and a lot of bowing and scraping to those in higher positions. Although Nigeria has one of the best doctor/patient ratios in Africa it also has one of the highest maternal mortality rates: 1250+ mothers die per 100,000 births. This is almost the same as Sierra Leone which is one of the worst health providers in the world due to the recent wars. I get the impression that many of the doctors are sitting behind desks either in the governments, universities or senior managerial positions and are thus not really available to patients.

Nurses are the backbone in palliative care, even in the developed countries. However, in order to practise palliative care in any country they need the respect and support of their medical colleagues. It will be a mammoth task to get this instilled in Nigeria, which is a very proud nation and proud of what they have achieved and of their people who are very smart. Many of these have put their intelligence into helping their fellow Nigerians but others have used their intellect to deceive and gain money for themselves.

Sadly, Nigeria has a very bad name on the international scene and donors very often refuse to give money to Nigeria. This is because corruption is still rife ever since the Biafran war when people had to steal to survive. There is now almost a national acceptance of corruption and I suppose it is very hard and requires a lot of integrity, if you are brought up in such a society not to be corrupt yourself. Nigeria has had a succession of leaders. Some bring good but often very bad things to the country. There have been many executions of government opposition members and of people who speak out against the leaders in power.

Some of the best writers in Africa are Nigerian and many of them have left the country of their birth to preserve their own safety and that of their families. Some have recently returned but it depends on the attitude of the government of the day. The suffering that occurred during the Biafran War has been well documented in such books as Chimamanda Ngozi Adichie's *Half of a Yellow Sun*.[48]

Following an advocacy visit in 2005 when we were introduced to some medical doctors who could bring advocacy to the government, we heard about a pharmacist who was head of the National Drug Authority. This lady had worked incessantly to bring safe drugs to Nigeria. One of the corrupted practices we find in many countries is that drugs are brought in from abroad from unscrupulous manufacturers. Both the manufacturers in countries such as India and the procurers in the country receiving the drugs gain from this practice but the patients die, and India is the country most criticised for this practice.

In Uganda there have even been medicines labelled as containing a certain ingredient yet on analysis none of the correct and labelled ingredients can be found. Many times these firms will offer a bribe to the procurer in the country. The brave Nigerian lady pharmacist I mentioned above went to India to sort out these drug firms and really cleared up the medical scene, but this made her very unpopular with the people who were gaining from this corrupt practice and she had a strong opposition. She would be a formidable partner in any debate and she has the respect of many, but her life was threatened because of her integrity.

In 2006 morphine powder was imported for the first time into Nigeria. It is still only available to a small percentage of Nigerian palliative services or hospitals because formal distribution has not been organised. Nigeria formed the Hospice and Palliative Care Association of Nigeria (HPCAN) at a conference in Abuja in January 2007. This organisation is run completely by volunteers in different parts of the country. It has made little progress due to financial constraints but I understand they recently received a grant to open an office in Abuja.

Several small hospices have commenced. But there is no model as yet for Nigeria. UCH Ibadan has a vision to become the Makerere for West Africa for palliative medicine and hold distance learning courses in

---

[48] Chimamanda Ngozi Adichie, *Half of a Yellow Sun*, Fourth Estate Ltd, 2006.

palliative medicine. The Centre for Palliative Care in Nigeria (CPCN) would then be the model.

But Nigeria has one big plus. If a Nigerian really takes something on board they can move it and the women are the best at this! We have had two pharmacists and nurse and doctor counterparts on two of our programmes for initiators in Africa. The pharmacists attended a special programme for pharmacists on procurement and making up of morphine followed by distribution through a government. This was in 2009 and already they are making a difference.

Palliative care is now in Lagos, Ibadan, Abeokuta, Zaria, Enugu and Ilorin. It is moving but there is so much to be done.

Cameroon

We first became interested in assisting Cameroon when George Ndenikum, a nurse with the Baptist mission in Bamenda, attended the first Distance Learning Diploma course in Kampala. George returned and initiated a palliative care team. Bamenda is in the English-speaking part of Cameroon. This is a country that was occupied both by the British and the French. The English-speaking side is the side closest to Nigeria and the French contains the two largest cities, the capital city Yaoundé and Douala. Both English- and French-speaking sections live in harmony.

This country has been relatively peaceful with no history of war since independence. Dr Jagwe and I visited there in January 2004 with a view to bringing advocacy to the government and training schools as well as visiting the new team at Banso Baptist Hospital (BBH), Kumbo in Bamenda Province. We were also taken to a production centre run by the Baptist mission where they made liquids for intravenous use as well as bottled water which they sold for the mission. This production unit was run by pharmacists and they agreed that when morphine was imported they would make up affordable morphine according to the Blue Book.[49]

Professor Tih had met us in Yaoundé with a view to our talking to the government people but he had another agenda and we were the people in waiting. This kind of thing is exasperating and happens frequently in Africa. You put a lot of funds and planning into meeting

---

[49] For more details about the Blue Book, see the final section of Chapter 11.

officials and are then frustrated by a parallel agenda, even when you have been assured that all is in place before you leave Uganda.

When we visited the government offices in Yaoundé, we were disappointed to find we only had one day, most of which was spent in waiting rooms. It also happened to be the day when people were expected to come and wish a happy new year to the head of state. Thus the waiting time was long and we left the capital without seeing the people we needed to see. Prof Tih said '*Hakuna matata!*'[50] If we wrote out the proposal he would take it himself and present it to the Government. The proposal we wrote for Cameroon was researched and is now used as a template for assessing each country as we move into it. The most recent one for Rwanda can be found below as Appendix D.

We were wonderfully surprised when we found out twelve months later that morphine was being imported! Another example of how even the things that frustrate us at the time can turn into something good. God is there somewhere! But we do not always realise or acknowledge that his plans are not always our own.

We spent most of our time in Cameroon driving on roads in beautiful scenery littered with the wrecks of cars which hadn't made it as successfully on that journey. The journey to Banso Hospital from Bamenda was only a couple of hours but it was quite a scary ride with the ravine dropping. As we got to the hospital there were pictures on the walls of *m'zungus* who had died on that road, remembering them in death.

Morphine is now being supplied to Baptist hospitals by the Baptist production unit. Meanwhile Hospice Africa UK was supporting this small venture with kick-start funding. The initial kick start was to give them time to get funding from other sources. But this did not happen for several reasons, not least because West Africa is often avoided by donors because of the history of corruption. Further support was given to BBH in November 2007 when Catherine spent a month with the team assessing and sharing standards and methods of keeping reports. She trained the team at that time.

A follow-up visit was organised for February 2008 when Catherine Nawangi and I would go to Cameroon together to assess the situation. This second visit was a bit of surprise because, as I stated previously, it had always been a peaceful country. Our flight from Nigeria arrived at 11

---

[50] This means 'no problem' in Swahili which they do not speak in Cameroon! Swahili is the unifying language for East Africa.

pm and by midnight the roads of the country had been closed in an effort to show the government that enough was enough. The background to this demonstration was that Cameroon had had the same president for more than twenty years, during which time the cost of living had increased but there had been no rise in salaries. Indeed on one occasion salaries were even reduced.

Shortly before the demonstration the government had put up the price of oil. Now Cameroon produces its own oil. As we are aware, when the price of oil increases the cost of all commodities necessary for even the poorest person increases. Taxi drivers and the drivers of buses decided to bring the country to a halt and stopped traffic on the roads. In order to do this they recruited many young people who were out of work.

We managed to get from the airport to the Baptist hostel in Douala where we were to stay, arriving at 2 am. We were given strict instructions to be up by 4 am. Obediently we got up to find that we were waiting for a group of American and Canadian Baptists who would be accompanying us. These guys were in top form, well rested and had already visited some places. So we all climbed into the bus and then one of the guys suggested we should buy some croissants for our breakfast. We stopped at a French patisserie and after getting our food we started up again.

After going over the bridge out of Douala we saw a fire that was lit from one side of the road to another. Our fearless driver just kept going while many of us were oblivious, eating our croissants. We suddenly became aware of hostile voices shouting at us from the road and bangs on the side of this beautiful bus with Cameroon Baptist mission written on the side. Our driver, who had tended to go fast, came to a halt.

Suddenly a stone smashed into the window beside me. Automatically standing up I was grabbed down on Catherine's lap beside me. The Vietnam veteran in front of me was so frightened. Another stone had hit the windscreen but the driver could still see as it was above his vision. Pressing on to the clutch, he reversed and managed to get us out of there and flew like the wind back to the hostel while everybody else shook like leaves.

When we got back we realised the guest house did not provide food but the lady in charge would occasionally let guests go into the kitchen and cook. In the next three days the Cameroon team would go out before sunrise to buy food from some of the small shops that were open and so we certainly did not lack something every day to eat.

We were there for four days before we were able to book flights out of the country, and had a military escort to the airport. Was this an abortive attempt by us to help Cameroon and carry out more advocacy? No, George and Catherine and I spent several hours each day at the computers, discussing the progress of the palliative care team and planning training programmes, giving George PowerPoint presentation documents to help him. We also made friends with the group members. We encouraged George not to miss the opportunity to raise awareness of the needs for palliative care and for funding. His team was literally funded only from HA. So we arranged for George to give a presentation to the other people about the need for palliative care and what they were doing.

The pathologist and his wife who was a nurse from Seattle took our information and promised to try to raise funds which would go to HA(USA) and would be sent to George and his team. We returned to Uganda and were very happy to get home safely.

We then carried out a full assessment in September 2008 and found a difficult situation. The original team trained by Catherine had moved on for varying reasons. The Banso palliative care team was being supported by a VSO nurse with experience, but she returned home shortly after our visit. George himself was running around the Baptist hospitals trying to bring advocacy for palliative care and was then not able to support them because he was spreading himself too thin.

The saddest thing was to see poor patients coming for treatment and going away without their medicines because they could not afford the price. Also the cost of the morphine was five times more for them than in Uganda. The problems we find on the ground are difficult and need constant monitoring to continue a service that is loving and holistic and really cares.

However, we found that the palliative team in the provincial hospital in Bamenda Town had a small but excellent palliative care team. This was the Government Hospital but they were able to follow up patients in home care because Dr Jonah Wefuan, the Director of the hospital was so interested in palliative care and meeting the needs of the patients in the hospital. Dr Jonah was also now a member of the Board of the African Palliative Care Association. Two nurses were working in a small area and going to see patients in the wards. When they needed to do home visits, the hospital car would be used but if not available Dr Jonah would lend his own car. It was a service based on hospitality and generosity with love.

In 2009, a VSO doctor was posted to Banso to help George. She is Catherine d'Souza and her husband is an administrator and recently qualified as a physiotherapist. They met up with us at the AGM in 2008 and we arranged for them to have a few weeks in Kampala before leaving for Cameroon. They were an inspirational couple and left us with great expectations. Their first months were most frustrating for them as they were unable to move things forward.

Figure 22.10   *Group involved in training programme for health professionals held in Provincial Hospital Bamenda, 2008. Front row, 4th from left: George Ndenikum, Palliative Care Leader at Banso Hospital; 5th from left: Catherine Nawangi, Clinical Trainer for International Programmes; 6th from left: Dr Jonah Wefuan, Medical Director of Provincial Hospital Bamenda; 7th from left: Dr Ndiforchu Victo, Regional Delegate of Public Health.*

However the Palliative Care Association of Cameroon was begun in early 2009, under the presidency of Dr Jonah Wefuan, now retired from his role as Director of the Provincial Hospital in Bamenda Town. There was a need for a good teacher to be part of the new association to take the knowledge of palliative care to the rest of Bamenda and Cameroon at large. George was posted to this area in 2009 and in 2010 Banso is catching up and seeing more patients with a dedicated service now under the leadership of Dr Catherine Nawangi who is training a Cameroonian to take over from her. Catherine and Dr Eddie Mwebesa, our home-grown specialist registrar in Uganda, are going to join Catherine in the visit to West Africa in May 2010. It is so important to keep up with each struggling service and assist them in maintaining standards.

Sierra Leone

In 2005 Dr Jagwe and I were invited to join a team supported by Help the Hospice in London and APCA to visit Shepherd's Hospice in Sierra Leone. This is a beautiful country which was destroyed as a trade-off from the war in Liberia. The whole war boiled down to diamonds. Although they had all of the diamonds, coveted by Liberia and their neighbours, they are now the poorest country in the world according to the Human Development Index in 2008. During this visit, there was no water or electricity in the capital. Signs of the war were everywhere, ex-soldiers 'gone for top'[51] wandered the streets. Most of them were harmless but quite on edge when they approached white people, demanding their rights.

People of all ages were seen without arms and legs. There was a special area in the capital where these people were being rehabilitated. The atrocities carried out in Sierra Leone were well documented and they seemed to be the worst of all the atrocities of recent wars. On this trip we were joined by Nick Pahl from Help the Hospices in London, and Sambhulo Mukwananzi (Sam), a nurse from Island Hospice in Harare, Zimbabwe. Nick had a great sense of humour but was thoroughly shocked by his first visit to an African country.

Shepherd's Hospice was founded in 1994, but had been struggling throughout the war years and ever since. Gabriel who founded the hospice and is still CEO, in order to keep it as a going concern, has been completely donor-driven, so much so that you would hardly recognise it as a hospice. There are two very large three-storey buildings. One houses the offices and on the ground floor a small clinic, part of which is palliative care. The rest are offices of those organising services for vulnerable children and women, and TB and AIDS patients. Most of the donors do not give any funding to the palliative care aspect. Over the years many people have visited this hospice but have been mainly from the UK. Training from the UK has been on an ad hoc basis. And each time they train they leave quickly afterwards and then the team changes;

---

[51] Pidgin English expression for a confused state.

new people come in and struggle without training, and this cycle keeps recurring.

When people come from the rich West to teach palliative care in an African country without knowledge of the culture or economy of the country, and without leaving planned follow up or training the trainers in country, palliative care seldom takes root. We have seen this happen in several countries including Senegal, Ghana and the Gambia. However having said that, things are moving all the time and by the time this book is published these countries may be moving towards a service. The first move from Sierra Leone to have African training was when they sent their nurse Charles Munda to HAU in 2007 for a week's health profession course followed by three weeks' training with the clinical team. He returned to Sierra Leone very inspired.

Figure 22.11 *Esther Walker and Dr James Russell with a patient in Freetown, 2007.*

With the help of Esther Walker, a palliative care nurse married to head of security in British High Commission, the palliative care team was moving and giving good care to patients and families. Esther was giving her time voluntarily to Shepherd's Hospice and did a wonderful job carrying out training and working with the local people to set up the Palliative Care Association of Sierra Leone. But I am getting ahead of myself. Back to that visit with Help the Hospices in 2005.

While we were in Freetown we visited the University Medical School and in the Department of Medicine we were introduced to a young doctor, Dr Russell. In fact there were only two people in that department. Nick offered to pay for Dr Russell to come to Hospice Africa for three months' training, so he would be a leader with clinical skills in the palliative care section at Shepherd's Hospice. He agreed to do so and spent the three months working closely with our team and was very popular with the Ugandan team.

However, just before he left he was informed he had been accepted to do two years' training in cardiology in South Africa. We were very upset because he had been our new hope for Shepherd's Hospice. Shortly after this, fellowships were being offered to bring people to the collaborating centre in Wisconsin, USA, where they would have a week's training in advocacy to assist their countries to bring in morphine. The chief executive applied and was chosen to be the representative of Sierra Leone. (Morphine powder was eventually imported late in 2008. It is now in use in a pilot with Dr Russell supporting the team.)

In February 2008 I visited Sierra Leone again, hosted by Esther Walker. There we found Charles working with a new clinical officer and a nurse who had been there for a year. Within the previous six months I had been approached by a reporter from *The New York Times* who was writing a feature article on the availability of morphine for pain control in African countries. He asked me what country he could visit where they didn't have morphine so he could see the extent of the pain that was not being relieved. I advised him to go to Shepherd's Hospice in Sierra Leone. He went there and wrote a very moving article. He had been taken on home visits by a nurse (Stephen) who impressed him so much.

So when I got to Shepherd's Hospice I asked where this nurse was, only to be told he had left with a disagreement with the Manager. This again was history repeating itself. Sadly Stephen developed cancer shortly after he had left. He was in severe pain and it took forever for him to get a biopsy and the results of the biopsy. When the hospice heard that he had cancer, the lady nurse in the team went to visit him. She was met by Stephen's father who was extremely angry with the hospice. The family believed that the hospice had put witchcraft on him and wanted no help. Very distressed, the nurse returned and was told that Stephen would not be given any help from this team. This of course is completely against the ethos and does not take into account the recognised stages of grief the families go through.

However, later Esther made contact. The family accepted for her to visit Stephen and she was doing her best to control the pain with Tramadol, the only stronger analgesic available. I actually visited him and we got the story from a very sympathetic father and they were so thrilled with the help they had received from Esther. At this point Stephen had had his biopsy but had not yet received the result. He gave me the name of the doctor, who coincidentally I had met the day before at a surgeon's meeting in Freetown. He had given me his card with his number. I called him and told him that Stephen had been trying to get in touch.

Sadly the news was not good. The biopsy showed he had a rapidly progressive nasopharyngeal cancer and needed radiotherapy urgently. There was no radiotherapy in Sierra Leone and they were trying to get him to go to Ghana for this. Later we heard that before Stephen managed to raise the money to go to Ghana, he had died. This indeed was a sad story. But maybe Stephen is looking down on us and helping Shepherd's Hospice.

On a positive note, during my February 2008 visit, Dr Russell was back from his cardiology training and I met him in Freetown. He promised to come and accompany us on home visits. We were very impressed with his approach to the patients and he promised to come on a regular basis and support the team. On the last day of my visit I was asked to discuss ethos and the problem of Stephen from which we should all learn that we must help everybody.

The team that I spoke to included the whole team of Shepherd's Hospice even if they were working on other projects besides palliative care. We offered to bring the new clinical officer and nurse for similar training that Dr Russell had. This was agreed. However, a few months later we were told the nurse was unable to come for personal reasons and then in July in the UK I was able to speak to Gabriel on the phone; he told me that the clinical officer could not come, also due to personal reasons. The personal reasons were that they had both left, leaving Charles alone. Charles had no transport for the palliative care service.

During the months around our visit to Sierra Leone, a proposal had been given by the Shepherd's Hospice to the Department for International Development (DFID), for a palliative care grant. This proposal was mainly covering TB throughout the country. In fact they were successful with their application, but this was a worry as it indicated that TB and palliative care were synonymous.

News from Charles was scant after this visit, then we heard that he had left to pursue medicine in the University of Freetown. We were happy for him but he had been the leading light at the hospice. However, a new face appeared at our training programme in 2009. Francis Kamara came, full of enthusiasm and enjoyed the five weeks sharing with others from five African countries and went back even more enthusiastic. We are about to visit them again as this goes to press and Catherine has been invited to spend a month with them later this year, working on the ground and sharing experiences.

Sudan

Sudan is one of the largest countries in Africa. Most of the population (30 million) is centred in the North and in the capital Khartoum. Ten million of the population are in the South. Elections are in progress as I write and many prayers are said for peace, *Inshallah!*[52] It is a Muslim country with Christianity being the second religion. Most Christians are in Khartoum or in the South. The South has been trying for many years to be independent from the North but because of the oil wealth being mainly in the South they have had wars and suffering, particularly for the South.

The low population density means that some villages are separated from the rest of the country by desert so that it is impossible to travel by road and out of their economic range to fly to Khartoum for treatment. Many are dying in agony in these places.

Sudan was first brought to our attentions when Esther Walker, who had assisted so much in Sierra Leone, moved with her husband's work to Khartoum. Ever vigilant for the palliative care needs in the country she was stationed in, she began to write to us about the needs there in the cancer hospitals and to make contacts with the people there. As we were to learn later on a visit, the two cancer hospitals in the country were in or near Khartoum and anyone else in this huge country had to travel there if they needed treatment. This meant a very small proportion of those in need of cancer treatment in the country were reaching any form of curative therapy. Many who eventually reached the hospital were about to die and we can only guess how many set out and died on the way. Remember that they would be in terrible pain with advanced cancers.

---

[52]'Please God' or 'God willing' in Arabic

So Esther started to visit the cancer hospitals and made contact with the oncologists. One in particular was Dr Nahla Gaffer, a radiotherapist from the Radiation and Isotope Centre of Khartoum (RICK). This lady was a very special person, with a real heart for the suffering she had witnessed and fire in the belly to do something about it. Against many odds, she came to Uganda for the international training programme in October 2009. She was an inspiration to the class, attended all the programmes and brought up many interesting ideas in the discussions. She was accompanied by a nurse, Adam Al Faki, from the Soba University Teaching Hospital. The language in Khartoum is Arabic. Nahla's English was very good and she helped Adam with understanding the lectures as his English was poor on entry but much improved after the five weeks!

Before the two returned at the end of the course, the funding for a visit from Dr Jagwe and me had been obtained and we visited in January of this year (2010) to bring advocacy, or really to reinforce Nahla's advocacy with the Government, the pharmacists and the hospitals involved with cancer. Subsequently Catherine Nawangi spent a month with them. Nahla, Esther and Adam were carrying it forward and training programmes had begun with great enthusiasm. It is now only six months since we first met Nahla, and Khartoum is moving forward both in training and in service.

Figure 22.12   *Dr Nahla Gaffer(right) in the pharmacy at the
                    Radiation and Isotope Centre, Khartoum (RICK).*

Meanwhile in December 2009, Catherine and another of our nurse trainers, Mwazi, went to Southern Sudan at the invitation of a Catholic Mission Hospital and the Camboni Sisters, to assist with training for spiritual advisors in end of life care.

Francophone Africa

In July 2008 I was invited to Lyon, France, to present a paper on our work at a research meeting at the WHO Research Centre. An African Oxford Cancer Foundation (AfrOx) meeting was piggy-backed onto this meeting. AfrOx is a group of concerned researchers and clinicians from Oxford UK who are trying to assist the need of cancer patients in Africa. The immediate need for the millions suffering cancer pain and in need of palliative care was brought forward. It was at this meeting, attended by representatives from all over Africa, that we realised there was a need to extend the coverage of palliative care to Francophone and eventually Lusophone Africa. HAU had been a good model for Anglophone African countries and was moving, albeit slowly. If we look at the map of PC coverage in 2006 (see above, p. 228) we note that most of the Francophone countries fit within those countries with no or little provision for palliative care.

Here was a need that we had not addressed. We then wrote a concept paper which was originally written for AfrOx, but with little response, and which has been used to address other donors. It was then the basis for the development of a new arm in France: Hospice Africa (Soins Palliatifs) France. The concept note for these countries is in English and French. The Blue Book was already translated into French and being given out to Francophone countries but they needed basic training and a palliative care service suitable to their health systems and reaching the most vulnerable.

It was perceived that a feasibility study was necessary. The countries mooted as being ready for the study were as follows:

Congo Brazzaville: we met a reverend Sister from there with her link doctor in France in June 2009. They have a support service poised for palliative care but without specific training and the required medications including oral affordable morphine.

Cameroon: from above, it might seem the right country. Here there are Anglophone and Francophone areas where some speak both languages. We already have a service in the Anglophone area (Banso in Bamenda). We see that a Francophone model would have to be in the Francophone sector. We visited the Francophone sector on our most recent visit, as well as the University of Cameroon at Yaoundé. But we need Francophone people of vision to carry this forward.

Côte d'Ivoire has been trying and I understand from APCA has a good support service on the ground. They do not have the medications required as yet.

Rwanda is our neighbour so near enough to learn from the model in Uganda. They are bilingual *but* recently declared to be Anglophone. However this would not stop them being a model for a country with a Francophone history and language. We have seen people coming to Uganda for five years to see how we do it and yet it has still not taken off. They were waiting for the policy to come through the Ministry of Health. This has now come to fruition and they are posed to commence. But the permission for the Minister of Health has still not come to import affordable morphine. Rwanda has a much greater burden for cancer patients than for AIDS for palliative care. Also they have no provision for chemo or radiotherapy so everyone in need dies without treatment unless they can afford to leave the country to go to South Africa or further abroad. Some, the poorer, will come to Uganda. It is a difficult and tragic situation.

Rwanda is also a very small country, population 10 million, but has a high population density and little land left for even the Rwandans abroad to come back. However they have a well constituted health system and 95% of the population access it. There is HIV support at every health centre and the ARVs can be given in these centres by specially trained nurses.

So Rwanda is poised to be a model if they have the commitment to raise the funding initially and start with a free-standing hospice which can be the centre for training and for spreading the care throughout the health system.

Dr Jagwe and I visited Rwanda in December 2009 and returned with great expectations. Dr Jagwe has also attended their recent meeting about the policy document. We brought over the Nursing Sister, Grace Mukankuranga, the only nurse with palliative care training in the country, for further experience both of clinical palliative care and of the different types of services in Uganda. She is to be the nurse to commence the first hospice. She will be supported by Rose Gahire, head of the

Palliative Care Association of Rwanda (PCAR). Ruth Wooldridge, who commenced Nairobi Hospice is also assisting them with advice.

So what is our role in all this? We do not plant hospices. We assist those who are planting them with advocacy, advice and sharing experiences. We also try to put them on the right track for funding. In the last two years we have had three training programmes for initiators of palliative care in their own countries. These have proved to be very useful. Broadly speaking, the first two weeks are formal teaching with sharing sessions on how each country is or will be implementing. The second two weeks are tailored to the needs of the individual participants. The nurse and clinical officer receive clinical experience at the three HAU hospices as well as some insight into management of a free-standing hospice. The pharmacists get time regarding procurement and visiting the different areas in Kampala involved with procurement and reconstitution of oral morphine, and the acquiring the affordable medications required. The doctors get a mixture of home and hospital visits and organisation of services, including the public health approach and visits to the Ministry of Health.

The final week is training of trainers (TOT). This is so that the participants can return to their own countries, having learnt to pass on their skills. We learn so much from each other.

Figure 22.13 *The light is coming to Rwanda: a training group who have completed DELTA (Development Education Leadership Team in Action) at Kirambi Community Health & Development Programme, Rwanda, run by MMM, praying for peace.*

23   The Unforeseen

Fortunate are you when people hate you,
when they reject you and insult you
and number you among criminals,
because of the Son of Man.
Rejoice in that day and leap for joy,
for a great reward is kept for you in Heaven.
Remember that is how the ancestors
of this people treated the prophets.
(Luke 6:22–23)

A S CHILDREN we read about champions of different causes. For me, coming from a Catholic childhood, the lives of the saints would always leave us aghast as to how they managed to remain holy in such an unholy world. But today's world is very different than the world of my childhood and very different from the world of the saints. I have people that I call friends, people that are very strong characters and make a great difference in the world by their writing, public speaking or by moving forward in one field or another with integrity. Some of these have been such strong personalities that they are very difficult to live with and yet, difficult as they are, they have been able to give many gifts to other people by their inspiration.

From reading of the lives of people who have started religious congregations, I know that Dame Cicely – who started the wonderful modern hospice movement and has written about her soul-searching as to whether to commence a religious order for this work, so close is it to the spiritual aspects of life and death[53] – also passed through a time of personal suffering when withdrawing from the day-to-day work at St Christopher's.

There comes a time of suffering for most, perhaps no longer valued for the great work they have done by the people closest to them. People

---

[53] Clark David, *Cicely Saunders – Founder of the Hospice Movement, Selected Letters 1959–1999,* Oxford University Press, 2002.

like Bishop Shanahan of Nigeria were maligned verbally and died very sad over accusations, many of which were false. This world can be cruel and the bush telephone (or Chinese whispers) still operates in Africa among the international community. It is very lonely for souls who have struggled to help others with integrity and find that they have no friends. But I have been blessed with many friends and some I thought were friends until the Chinese whispers reached them.

How can we cope when even the work we have done is rubbished by others? And what causes others to rubbish history that has moved things for the good particularly? Going down this route and spending time wondering why a person would do this is quite destructive; it leads to sleepless nights and puts a damper on new initiatives.

I have experienced both of these and continue at times to experience these. So why haven't I had a nervous breakdown? Maybe that is still yet to come.

'God's silence makes you whole, for he alone can calm your troubled mind.'

If I can get away into silence and just reflect on similar situations in the past, I realise that at times I could see no way out of a situation and yet these difficulties often led to a greater leap or a change of direction which was so obviously meant to be. This has confirmed my belief in a God who is in control and that the work of Hospice Africa has been confirmed by Him as part of His plan for the poor and needy of Africa.

Having said that, I know when I have been maligned and I am hurt. God has blessed or cursed me with sensitivity to the attitudes of others towards me. I can tell when somebody has a reservation or becomes wary towards me.

So how can we continue to move forward when unforeseen problems arise that affect the very soul of the initiators? I am stating this not only for myself but for the initiators who supported me with a full heart and have done so for years and suddenly realise that the work can be destroyed so quickly and easily by people with another agenda.

Uganda has changed very rapidly within the last few years. When we arrived it was a poor country, devastated by war and sickness, yet the people had hope and were working together towards the future. They had lived for many years when they didn't know whether they would survive to the next day. Our nurses tell me there were bodies strung along the roads as they went to school in the morning. Through twenty years of oppressive regimes, people were killed and tortured indiscriminately and so people lived for the day and cared very much for their families and close friends. Hospice was welcomed with open arms and our initial teams were selfless when they saw the difference we could make to those in need with so little.

Now after 17 years we are so much bigger, and staff numbers have increased rapidly along with the salaries. We are still blessed with many dedicated team members and we thank God for that.

So how do we keep going in such a climate? Well, first of all why did we start in the first place in what appeared to be such a hopeless situation? We believe that God loves the poor in a special way, and He cares for the suffering. He is using us to help them. But we must always remember in Africa that what we do today might be destroyed tomorrow so we need to live, doing our best each day for we know not tomorrow. Secondly, we can see enough dedication in many of the teams to encourage us to continue. All people have good in them and all communities have good and bad. This is not particular to Uganda but is the same all over the world.

St Francis Xavier remarked that there is no greater suffering than to watch what one has built up for God being smashed down by man.

So how do I personally cope?

The biggest source of stress for me has been working with people who disagree with us, without having found out what we are and hope to achieve, even to the point of rudeness. I find rudeness very difficult to accept and prefer to sit down and discuss things calmly rather than keep disagreement hidden and continue to keep banging heads.

So how do I cope? First of all, I am very human and get upset. I try not to answer immediately but if I do, I get very angry. I lose sleep worrying about it for a few days following such an occasion. But when I eventually come to terms with it, I know it happened for a reason and that God is often directing me through this suffering in another direction or taking a different way to reaching conclusions that would touch our care for the patient and family.

As my life has changed over the last few years and I try to pass over the organisation of HAU to others I find that I am working just as hard. More and more of my time is being spent sending and receiving email, communicating with people from all over Africa. I find it difficult to fit in emails every day. Many need instant replies. Others include papers,

PowerPoint documents or policies I must track, due to their importance and influence on the delivery of palliative care in other African countries.

So how do I relax? Do I play games, do I walk? Although I jogged and swam a lot in my middle age, I am unable to do this as much as my body declines. I do enjoy a walk every now and again but I'm not a compulsive walker as I was a compulsive jogger and swimmer in Singapore.

I do enjoy music and reading, though, and I read an average of one book a week. In particular the writings of Dame Cicely have supported and inspired me over the years. In dealing with spirituality and dying, other authors have assisted me with my understanding such as Scott Peck, Jeanne Vanier and Henri Nouwen who wrote *The Wounded Healer*.[54]

I love having friends and have made many new friends since the start of HAU. I enjoy it when the house is full and I also enjoy it when the house is empty (although the latter is not very often these days). My home in Uganda, which belongs to Hospice Uganda, is in a beautiful place overlooking Lake Victoria. Looking at the view is a great source of inspiration and peace for me.

At my house I have a family of young ladies originally brought in as house girls and they are now housekeepers and caterers. They are excellent at making cakes which they make on order. This has become so popular that my home is always full of the smell of freshly baked cakes. They do this to raise funds for hospice. These young ladies have been with me for so long that they have become my family; their children are my grandchildren and I am their JaaJaa.

What of my blood family? I have family in Liverpool, London, Brighton and Ireland. I am very attached to them and often see them when I am home. Some have visited from time to time. They have all been very supportive over the years. My brother, Fr Joseph Merriman, SDB, a Salesian Priest, has been a spiritual standby for most of my life.

Since 1994, I cannot remember taking a holiday but I look forward to my retreat. It is a time when I reflect on my relationship with God – have I moved closer or further in the past year? – and fill up with spiritual fuel for the coming year. Initially I attended the Namugongo Camboni Convent and Retreat Centre, outside Kampala for my retreats.

---

[54] Henri Nouwen, *The Wounded Healer: Ministry in Contemporary Society*, Image, 1979.

Sister Doreen Boland, a Sacred Heart Sister, was my personal director at that time and continued to be so on and off over the years.

After about three years I found the setting of a retreat centre was not for me. Having my spiritual director was fine because once you know each other it's a great support, but if you get someone new it might take the whole retreat just to get aligned. So I decided to do a retreat on my own – just me and God, in a getaway. My first one was in a hotel called 'the Ranch on the Lake' off the Entebbe Road in Kampala. It is now posh and expensive, but then it was a quiet hotel with little rondovels in the shape of an African hut with a thatched roof.

I told the staff that I wanted to keep quiet and they agreed to have my meals delivered to me. Sister Doreen would come to visit me several times during the retreat which helped a lot. When Sister Doreen was transferred to Joigny, France, to the home of Sophie Barat, the founder of the Sacred Heart Sisters of which she is a member, I decided to go to France for my retreats. This was beautiful in spite of the fact that I didn't know France very well and certainly didn't know French very well as I had failed French exams twice many years ago.

The first year was very inspiring as I learned about the life of Sophie Barat and the house I stayed in was the house in which she was born. Her father used to make the barrel for the wine and the hills surrounding the town are full of vineyards. This town had two Catholic churches, very big, very cold and very empty, even on Sunday. The French are very proud of their Catholic heritage but, like most of Europe today, there are very few 'practising' Catholics. What struck me was the fact that everything in this town was very old; the streets and the houses were all built centuries ago, and untouched by the Second World War, unlike England.

The second year I went to Joigny I was very brave. I actually hired a car and drove myself on the right hand side of the road for two hours to Joigny. Having the car gave me independence to move around and visit other villages and scenic spots. The second time I was there, the retreat house was much busier. There was a group of novices from Eastern Europe having a great time, which was impressive but not so conducive to the silence I was seeking.

There were two sisters from Ireland who joined me on the retreat the second day. Both were elderly, older than me, but we shared a lot together as they had been in Mbarara for many years. We went one day to a nearby town in search of an Orthodox monastery. This monastery was only started five years previously and had sisters from all over

Eastern Europe. The Orthodox Church has a recent history of suffering and yet these sisters were so peaceful. They run retreats in their convents but they also raise funds by selling their Orthodox icons.

It was their chapel that absolutely inspired me. When you looked up at the roof you could see they had painted everything in the Old Testament from Adam to the birth of Christ, and all of a sudden I felt part of this vast plan. These paintings are beautiful and have all been painted by the sisters themselves. I actually returned to see them this year, meeting up with one of the Orthodox sisters, who was from Scotland, and Jim Bennett, of HA France, who had been volunteering for Hospice in Uganda on and off for many years. Following my two years in Joigny, I didn't want to start with a new spiritual director and it suddenly struck me that I was now so old that I would have more peace if I was on my own relating to God. So I took eight days in Clifden in Connemara, Ireland, being very grateful to a friend who lent me a holiday home in the area. With my small hired car I was able to move to the most beautiful spots in the world and take long walks besides the lakes, between the mountains and sometimes never meeting a soul.

One day I walked over to Iomaidh (Omey) Island where you can only go when the tide is out and you have to get back before the tide comes back in. It was just me, the ocean, the sky and God. It was a wonderful experience. I had been given advice on the beautiful spots by a friend, Phil Moloney from County Clare. I had met Phil when she was an APSO (Agency for Personal Services Overseas) volunteer, teaching in a school in Mbarara and we had been in touch ever since. She had been out to visit us in Uganda. She loved walking and had actually climbed every mountain in Connemara and she gave me directions on my first day of retreat. I based this retreat on the talks given by Bishop Kevin Dowling from South Africa who had given seven inspirational talks in Uganda during the palliative care week in 2007. His inspirational centring prayer is being promoted amongst our palliative care teams as support to the ethos.

Centring prayer is essential to me. It is the ability to talk to God and draw on His strength on any occasion, from joyful to life-threatening. The ability to turn to Him when we feel helpless to assist our suffering patient, or when we can't meet that deadline which will make or break the future of the work. But to have this relationship with God, we need to cultivate it with silent reflection. This may be formal or informal. Mine is nowadays very informal!

Phil Moloney was instrumental in my going the second year to Donegal. Her sister, an artist, who has visited us in Kampala, was living with her family in Luxembourg but they had established a beautiful house in Donegal, Ireland, overlooking the Atlantic Ocean. This again was a most beautiful area where I could go out and be alone with God in His nature. In 2008 and 2009 I spent my retreat time in this house and the surrounding beautiful views including the Atlantic Ocean and the mountains. In 2009 I based my retreat on the writings of John O'Donohue. He had died in January 2008. I found his books and tapes very helpful.

The house was very peaceful, but because I had had a major run in with an opposing force just before I left, I found it difficult to sleep for the first four nights. This was not helped by the fact that I had an attack of bronchitis and then on the second day my front tooth fell out. So it was 'Hooray, it's only me and God looking at me!'

I was able to sort out the dentist very fast but I was unable to receive antibiotics until I returned to the UK the following week.

In spite of these difficulties I am able to look back on the week and think of it as having been a great comfort to me. In contrast to a holiday, the silence in those eight days was enough for me. But now that I'm getting older I might spend even longer on retreat.

Meditating on the future, it is easy to get depressed. But it is just as easy to be full of hope. Uganda has been my home and my place of vision for seventeen years. We never dreamt in 1993 that so much would have happened here and in other countries. God is leading us and now is sending messages about my closure. If I was younger I might think of moving to one of the other African countries and helping them achieve what has been achieved in Uganda. However, it is time for me to close the book.

So I will stay, in the words of Nancy in the musical *Oliver!* 'as long as He needs me', while praying that God will lead what He has begun for some more years so that those who are suffering in Africa will receive relief in their own country and in their own homes.

24 Passing the Baton

The race is about the baton not the runners ...[55]

I WAS FIFTY-SEVEN when we started hospice. And so within three years I was at the retirement age for women in my own country. Therefore I have been very mindful of the need to mentor and transfer knowledge and skills in order to ensure that we have a smooth transition for the next generation of leaders in Hospice Africa.

As a model we have grown very quickly, which brings its own stresses. The form of management in most other NGOs does not suit a patient-centred organisation. We have seen the problems arising from non-medical administrators leading hospitals in the West. It is essential that there is medical input in the leadership. We are now at the stage of looking again at our form of management to make it more suitable for the non-bureaucratic approach required for a team supporting the patient and family at the centre of care.

Within our hospice ethos we mention respect for each other and using each other's different gifts to support our patients and families. 'Every member of the team is precious and can be expected to support and to be supported in times of trouble. This caring within the team overflows to those we care for.'[56]

Passing the baton is part of the challenge and real test of leadership. This has not been an easy task in Uganda and other countries. A more interesting tale may be read in *Audacity to Love – the Sequel*! But I have faith in the future for Hospice Uganda and the many other hospices we are supporting in Africa.

Despite our rapid growth, our patients and families are still receiving excellent care. Indeed, to go on a home visit and see the difference that palliative care is making to the patient and family, is the most reassuring and inspiring experience. This is the proof that the baton is being passed on.

---

[55] First of ten principles of a relay race by Nigel Hetherington.
[56] Ethos and Spirit of Hospices in Africa, HAU, p. 3.

We now have 135 staff working with us in three hospices in Uganda. The clinical and education teams are doing wonderful work and I pray this will continue as time goes on.

There will always be challenges from administrative and organisational matters, and from bureaucratic demands that slow down the care of a patient who cannot wait! But these can be reduced if our team members understand and apply the ethos. We must not be tempted to see our work organised as an assembly line with results measured in numbers and not in the heart of those who do it, which is indeed more difficult to measure.

We must struggle to keep the heart of hospice, and ensure that hospice does not become like a hospital, where often the patient is at the bottom of the pile not the centre of care. We must move together by identifying needs with the public health approach at country level and then bringing a response to the individual in the home.

This is God's work and we came with a lot of faith in 1993. Faith will bring God's work to fruition in Africa.

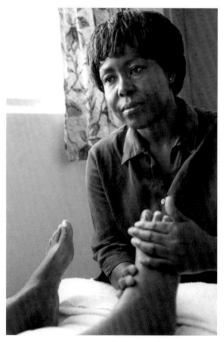

Figure 24.1 *A patient, now trained in reflexology, helps another patient.*

Figure 24.2 *Dr Siobhan Kennelly (right) from Ireland with Community Volunteer Workers, December 2004.*

Figure 24.3 *Fellowships from University College Dublin for Dr Maura Lynch MMM (front row, 2nd from left) and Anne for work in Uganda, 2007.*

*

We have met some tremendous personalities working with HAU, people who have really helped us. But one person in particular who I have already mentioned and whose personality and work have been a great asset to hospice is Dr Jack Jagwe. I'm sure Dr Jagwe won't mind my saying that he is six months older than me. He came to us in 1998, while he was the Chair of the National Drug Authority. He was the person at this time who suggested that Uganda law be changed so that the prescribers could be increased. He came to us as a highly respected physician who had been a leader in his field of medicine, of the National Teaching Hospital and in the Ministry of Health. He has lived through the difficult regimes of four presidents in Uganda and survived with humility and tranquillity.

Figure 24.4 *Dr Jack Jagwe (left) advocating in Nigeria.*

His time at hospice has not been easy for him. In the year 2000, when we received the grant from the Diana Fund to allow us to pursue the main mission of Hospice Africa, to support other African countries,

Dr Jagwe and I worked out a very successful way of approaching governments and training schools in each country. Over the next years, as I related earlier, we went to several African countries and as a result of these initiating visits, five of these countries imported morphine powder which allowed severe pain to be controlled by those initiating a service.

Dr Jagwe's contribution to this advocacy was strengthened by the fact that he was well known to the African governments, to medical personnel and to people involved with the drug authorities of each country. He trained himself in the documentation supporting advocacy for affordable oral morphine, through WHO documents and from our own history of making it work from Nairobi into now twelve countries in Africa. This was very useful.

He is a quiet gentleman who carries out his work in an unobtrusive way. He is humble and approachable. In this way his contribution to hospice and the initial mission has been tremendous. With the coming of the African Palliative Care Association (APCA) his advocacy was transferred to younger people within APCA itself. This lessened the impact of the initially successful advocacy. Sadly this transfer of advocacy issues was supported by the initial donors. There was an understandable struggle for APCA to become its own organisation but they were very quick to cut the umbilical cord from Hospice Africa Uganda, and in some ways threw out the baby with the bathwater. However it takes struggles to bring us back on keel and matters are moving well for both organisations today, with well demarcated responsibilities.

This was a hurtful period for many concerned. However, Dr Jagwe stuck in there and continues to be a trainer and advocate for morphine in other countries. In the University of Wisconsin they have developed a one-week training programme for advocates. The people running this programme have had very little exposure to palliative care in the developing world although very versed in morphine use in the epidemiological sense. Dr Jagwe has been invited to be a trainer in this programme, which is very useful to them with his vast experience.

25 Dying in Uganda

The dying know we are not God.
All they ask is that we do not desert them.[57]

Vex not his ghost: O, let him pass. He hates him
That would upon the rack of this tough world
Stretch him out longer.[58]

WHEN WE ARRIVED in Uganda in 1992 and 1993, an outstanding memory is the number of coffin makers at the roadside. Business was brisk. This was an indication of the money to be made even within a culture facing the deep tragedies of the AIDS epidemic.

Although our palliative care team visit our patients once a week on average and more frequently while controlling pain or towards the end of life, it is very rare to be with a patient when they are actually dying. It is very common to go out on a visit and find the funeral is in progress, and so for an expat like myself getting to know the customs surrounding death is more from discussion groups with the team than by personal experience. However, Lesley Phipps and I were with a young lady when she died and I would like to tell you about it.

The lady in question was from a very respected Catholic family with priests among her brothers. She herself was married to a highly respected doctor. She had four young children, after which the doctor went abroad for higher studies. While he was away she contracted HIV. Let's call the husband James and the wife Ann. James explained that she had contracted AIDS because the family was short of money while he was away. Now she was very ill and dying (this was before antiretrovirals were on the scene). The husband said that he was HIV negative and probably was because he has remarried since and is healthy.

---

[57] S. Cassidy, *Sharing the Darkness*, Darton, Longman & Todd, 1988, p. 64.
[58] Arden Shakespeare edition of King Lear, 2007, 5.3. 313–15.
51&52, both quoted from Jeffrey E, Jeffrey D, Vex not his Ghost: King Lear and end of life care, J R Coll Physicians Edinb 2009, 39.15-9.

It was a Sunday morning and all of us sat together; when Ann, being semi-conscious, began to gasp. This gasping is an occurrence before death but sometimes they revive at this point.

As soon as Ann started to gasp, James jumped up, grabbed a scarf and tied her chin up to the top of her head. Lesley and I were totally shocked because this stopped her from being able to breathe She passed away and when we asked him why he had done this, he explained that it was his culture in his tribe. We were made aware that culture comes above training!

People in Uganda don't always die gradually of a life-threatening disease. Death on the road must be one of the highest causes of death and leaves families devastated. Funerals are still one of the highest causes of absenteeism in Uganda and although it has been attributed to HIV/AIDS, sudden death is still high on the list of causes of death.

But for the Ugandan approaching death, there is so much suffering. First there is the fear, having seen so many others die in severe pain and knowing that although they have heard of the work of hospice they are unlikely to be the one in ten that receive such care today. Then there is the worry of what will happen to their children after death, which of their relatives will take their property and their children and perhaps treat them like slaves for their own family (a phenomenon which has only come up since the epidemic of death with AIDS). The fear that they are too weak to carry out the customary rituals to the ancestors, the fear they are cursed. Amongst all the worries, suddenly they are surrounded by many people. Some are friends but some are also their enemies, destroying their peace at the end of life. For it is the custom for the eagles to gather when someone is dying, although many times we cannot find someone to look after them during their illness ... This is the 'total suffering' so well described by Dame Cicely and so tangibly present in Uganda. To read more of the hardships for the years before ARVs became freely available in 2003, read the book by Peter Mugneyi.[59]

For a person to die in hospital is a family tragedy because transporting the body home is a huge price and sadly people in transport take advantage of the bereaved. I have said previously that people like to die at home so they are with their families and can be buried with their ancestors in the back garden. However, the home where they die may be far away from the village and the ancestors and if the body has to be

---

[59] P. Mugenyi, *Genocide by Denial*, Fountain Press, Kampala, 2008.

carried a long way to the village or needs to be kept for some days for relatives coming from abroad, the body needs to be embalmed.

Most people will do it the traditional way; this is usually buying a weak solution of formalin. The blood is drained from one of the veins and then this solution is injected into another vein. However a much easier way for those at home is to inject kerosene into the body cavities including the abdomen and thorax. Kerosene is cheap and it works.

Figure 25.1 *Remembering Daddy: memorial service at Hospice Uganda, November 2009.*

It is the custom with hospice to visit the home during the day of mourning before the burial to bring a small financial contribution to the family. They also give a card to get in touch with us if they have any problems following the funeral. It seldom happens that they come back to us. This is because in Uganda and other countries with traditional and restricted economies, there is a traditional fixed time for mourning which includes the funeral. During this time the nearest and dearest are expected to cry except for the men. Sometimes even professional criers come in. When this period is over, usually only a few days, they are expected to move on. They have to go work in the field, children have to be fed, there are no washing machines and dishwashers, except for the very rich, and life goes on. There is no time to sit around and be sorry for oneself.

There is a need for some research here to find if there are other needs but many of these needs are met in the traditional way. The African culture in each tribe has a way of dealing with most family problems including bereavement. They are often no different to our own but they work better most times.

I do resent people from the West trying to treat Africans as if they are the same and their needs are the same as their own. For example, Kenya Airways had a crash in West Africa and sadly all the lives were lost. So immediately counsellors were dispersed to the site for the relatives who came to claim the bodies of the deceased. All the families wanted was to collect the bodies and get home to carry out the funeral rituals. They found counselling an unnecessary delay. They had learned to cope with death in the school of life. West is not always best.

Installing the heir has been the tradition after a person has died. This is the person who will take on the responsibilities of the deceased and will also have the respect of the families which was previously due to the deceased. A man is usually the heir to a man and a woman the heir to a woman. Because of the frequency of death during the AIDS epidemic and people being unable to afford a ceremony, the tradition has changed and the heir may be installed earlier, sometimes even on the day of the funeral.

Figure 25.2 *Coffin retail boomed
during the AIDS epidemic.*

26 So What About My Own Death?

When my life is finally measured in months, weeks, days hours,
I want to live free of pain, free of indignity, free of loneliness

Give me your hand, give me your understanding
Give me your love
And let me go peacefully
And help my family, to understand
To understand.[60]

IN PALLIATIVE care we are on the coalface of death. This leads me to some thoughts on how I would like to die.

At our training programmes we ask for the participants to fill in a questionnaire, as much for their own sakes as for ours. This asks them about what they would like for their own death? To die at home? Their family with them? Spiritual support? What would they fear most – dying or the time before death? Would they support euthanasia? These are deep thoughts that those of us who are over seventy really need to think about. Yet, even though medicine is geared towards cure, and death is looked on as a failure by many in the profession, we all have to die. We have a lifetime to get used to the idea but so many of us never do.

For those of us who do not die young, there is the added burden in old age of wondering if we will have a long protracted period of dependency prior to death itself. So many of us fear this, even more than death. I have worked in geriatric medicine and palliative care, and the final days of many of our elderly in the West today are not to be envied. Coming to terms with the possibility of being in a home for the aged anywhere in the world is difficult and something I have never come to accept with peace. This does not get easier as I see the trends in geriatric nursing in the Western world today. Perhaps I should stay in Uganda?

But I must be ready to go whenever God calls. I would like to see certain things completed and I would like to see our ethos penetrating

---

[60] Sung by Albert Au on the album SPHC Voices for Hospices, 2005.

across all palliative care services in Africa so that patients and families will feel the full effect of the caring that true palliative care brings.

Whenever the time comes, however, I must be ready to trust my God, who has brought about so many miracles, using our teams to carry this work forward for those suffering in Africa.

At the start of this chapter, I quoted the words of the very moving song sung by Albert Au. This is all we need to give others and all we need from those who are caring for us, when our time comes. The song involves the needs of the patient from the health workers but also thinking of the family left behind, who need comfort and to understand why I have to go.

So who will be my family when I die? Who will grieve for me? Who will be caring for me? Will I, like Dame Cicely and the lady in Cape Town, die in the care of my own hospice? I could think of nothing better. We have some of the best carers in the world here in hospice. But they are also my family, my daughters and granddaughters. My little family in Munyonyo are closest to me and they and their children will always be.

I also have daughters and grandchildren in Singapore and they continue to show me love and support in my old age.

I have been privileged to witness the good deaths and the bad deaths.

At the time of death we are in God's hands and of those we love and who love us. We hope to be united again in the next world. This will be the result of the 'Audacity to Love' each other.

Appendix A   Living while Dying

Anne Merriman, Health Services Coordinator, Nairobi Hospice, Nairobi, Kenya[61]

John was a patient referred to the Nairobi Hospice in November 1990. He died in May 1991. John had been in and out of hospital for several months before he was referred to us.

After the Hospice took over his care, he lived with his young family and continued to supervise the building of his house until a few days before his death. He was never admitted to hospital again. He told us, 'Before I met you I was dying ... Now I am living.'

John is one of 180 patients who have been cared over the last year and a half by the Nairobi Hospice, mainly at home. The ages of these patients ranges from two to ninety, although the average patient age is below that of hospice patients in the United Kingdom. Often cancer is very advanced when first seen, and patients suffer psychological pain due to changes in appearance, from advanced cancer of the face, for example.

The Hospice idea is new to Kenya, and ours is only the second hospice foundation in Sub-Saharan Africa.

We therefore have an extensive teaching programme reaching out to doctors, nurses, and volunteers in Nairobi and the provinces. Our aim is to bring pain relief, symptom control, and provide psychological support to all those in need throughout Kenya.

Our hospice care is provided free of charge, but most of our patients cannot afford their medication. Our problems include meeting the costs for these patients, and at the end of 18 months service we are greatly in need of funds to continue the work.

We are presently concentrating on consolidation of the hospice in Nairobi and the training of Kenyan staff. We hope to have a doctor in training by next year. Following this, we hope to help other provinces to set up hospices. Already there has been interest shown in Nyeri, Nakurru, and Mombasa.

As this is very much God's work, we are putting our trust in Him to continue what was begun with the courage of those who saw a need and established the Nairobi Hospice to meet it.

---

[61] First published in *Contact*, no. 122, October 1991, Christian Medical Commission, Geneva.

Appendix B

Do's and Don'ts for Volunteers and Health Workers

Don't

- Come thinking you are God's gift to Africa. You have a lot to learn from Africa too.
- Come as a reason for getting out of a difficult situation at home, e.g. a broken relationship, recent bereavement, difficulties at work.
- Come with the first offer you have. Research where you are going and if possible get references of the area or look at the website.
- Do not try to get your visa in your own country – you can get it very easily in Uganda, at the airport coming in.
- Think that acceptable clothing at home is acceptable here. There is a dress code, especially for women here.
- Wear mini skirts or shorts at formal occasions or in hospice, on home visits.
- Expose your belly button or the cleavage of your backside.
- Get drunk unless with someone you trust who can take you home.
- Travel on long journeys by bus exposing your goods; they are a temptation to those who have less.
- Leave money, cellphones or valuables where people can see them; again this is a temptation to those who have less.
- Leave your computer out in a hotel room or in your car – lock it up.
- Give out your personal details unless you know and trust the person.
- Get involved sexually with the locals unless in serious relationships. Casual contacts lead to AIDS.
- Stop if you have a road accident and someone might be hurt. Mob justice still rules! Keep going to the nearest police station.

Do

- Research your role and plan your days as much as possible.
- If volunteering try and raise funds for your stay and some for work you may want to do while here with patients or the team.
- Consider how this stay is going to fit into your life plans.
- If coming to HAU, let us know in good time, send your CV and discuss any questions before you leave home.
- If going to HAU or another hospice in a developing country, read *International Volunteering in Palliative Care: Tips to Get You Started*, a book for volunteers recently published by Help the Hospices.[62]
- Get your jabs and anti-malarial tablets in plenty of time before leaving.
- Ensure you have enough money for your stay.
- Take time off to relax and chill out. There are plenty of tourist places in Uganda and it is a beautiful country to explore.
- Come out with a friend if possible. It is easier to do things together than singly, although there are often plenty of people around for you to join in with.
- Remember you have come to give. However, you will receive more than you give in this experience of working with the very ill and assisting at the end of life.
- If not sure of how to behave or proceed, ask a trustworthy local friend.
- Be careful on the roads. Try not to drive immediately unless on the quieter side of town. Driving in Kampala is life-threatening these days!
- If you are going to use a *borda borda* regularly (not recommended) bring your own crash helmet.
- Make sure that you know the cost of your fare on the *matatu* before you get on.
- Ask the price of the taxi before you get in and bargain if it is too high. Know the local costs.
- In Uganda use the *Eye*, the local tourists book which comes out free monthly, to guide you and for useful telephone numbers

---

[62] *International Volunteering in Palliative Care: Tips to Get You Started*, London: Help the Hospices, 2010.

Appendix C

Ethos & Spirit of Hospices in Africa[63]

> 'How can I understand a figure or a statistic unless I have held the hand that it represents? The people we are talking about are the same as us. By the way we treat them, we know just how much like Jesus we have become.'
>
> Dr. J P Muliyil, Epidemiologist with CHAD, ECC, Velore, India, in Gillian Paterson, *Love in the Time of AIDS*, 1996.

Introduction

About Hospice Africa Uganda

Hospice Africa was registered as a charity in UK in August 1993. Hospice Africa (Uganda) commenced their service for patients and families on 23 September 1993. Hospice Uganda was registered as an NGO in October 1994.

Hospice Africa was conceived as a support group for an African Hospice which would be a model not only for the country in which it was based, but for all African countries so that hospice philosophy and care could be adapted to the cultural and economic requirements of each country.

Following a feasibility study of those African countries requesting hospice services, Uganda was chosen for the 'model' hospice.

The **objectives of Hospice Africa** and Hospice Uganda in 1993 and recently rephrased are:

---

[63] Anne Merriman, re-edited from 2000 edn on 15 April 2005 and 11 July 2009.

1. To provide an appropriate palliative care service to patients with cancer and/or HIV/AIDS and their families within defined operational areas.

2. To enable the provision of palliative care services in Uganda, through advocacy, education and training.

3. To facilitate the initiation and expansion of palliative care in Africa by providing an affordable African model.

The spirit of hospice/palliative care

'It is in giving, that we receive . . .'

The inspiration for hospice in Africa comes from the suffering patient and family. The centre of care is the love for patient and family and our concern to relieve suffering, support with love and to be there with them as long as we are needed.

The care arises from our own acknowledgement that we too are in need of care. That caring is an essential part of God's plan for the world and that caring and being cared for are two sides of the human condition that can make us fully human.

Hospice/palliative care, believes that the time before death is a special time for the patient and family, when hurts can be healed, secrets can be shared and true love based on the recognition of the uniqueness of each person is acknowledged. This includes the patients' beliefs. Hospice respects religious beliefs and is prepared to pray with patients and families of all religions.

The Team (including teams for hospice services and national organisations)

The hospice team is made up of health and non-health professional members and volunteers. The spirit of hospice is shown in the Latin word '*Hospitium*', or hospitality. This means that we are a family, showing love for each other and for those who visit us whether patients or visitors interested in our work and in helping our patients and families.

Every member of the team is precious and can be expected to support and to be supported in times of trouble. This caring within the team overflows to those we care for.

The word bureaucracy is anathema in hospice/palliative care. Management makes decisions after consultation with all concerned. News of visitors and major decisions are disseminated daily so that the whole hospice family is involved and prepared. The Board of Directors is kept informed and confirms major policy decisions.

Volunteers

Volunteers include Boards of Directors and those who come to give practical help. If possible, volunteers are requested to attend a course at a hospice suitable to their professional training. This allows them to see in greater depth several aspects of hospice and the new specialty of palliative medicine. Volunteers are also encouraged to go out with the team on home visits. This allows them to see the difference hospice can make to a patient and family.

It is most important that the spirit of volunteerism is understood. Selfless giving of self, without expectation of monetary reward, defines the hospice volunteer. Having said this, the rewards received from the patient and family and the experience of sharing this special time with them, bring rewards that are not measurable in this world.

The patient and family

> *The patient and family are our guests and have choices in their relationships with us including their treatments and which secrets they share. They are reassured that we will not abandon them whatever their choices.*

The relationship with the patient and each other is not authoritarian. Confidentiality and ethical issues are a priority.

Attention to detail

Because our patients are in a vulnerable position, attention to detail and immediate response to needs is essential. There cannot be a laid back attitude from the team. Each member must be prepared to take immediate action when the comfort of the patient and/or family is at stake.

This attention to detail is echoed in the administration and support for the medical team. This means that families are welcomed and attended to immediately. People waiting for attention are offered a drink to make them feel at home. Payment of invoices and attention to details are acted on immediately so that the support service is not suspended or our work held up for want of this attention.

Building on initiatives

New ideas or initiatives are often brought forward by the humbler members of the team. These should be listened to and changes made if the initiative will improve our patient care. Squashing of initiatives by a management can impede the growth of hospice and the adaptation to changes in society and culture.

The Management Team (or the Association Board)

Those managing a service or responsible as Board members of a hospice or national association must be able to demonstrate their loyalty to the needs of the patient and family. Each member must be of the highest integrity. Each is responsible, in their own way, for the continuance of the spirit of hospice/palliative care in the organisation. Their dedication will be rooted in their individual spirituality and selflessness in giving without reserve.

Hospice recognises the unique contribution of each member of the team to this special work. However, the individual development of the team members is encouraged as well as their usefulness to the team work.

Each member of Management will be aware that they must be an example to all and that decisions must be made without selfishness for themselves or immediate family, but with the good of all in need of our services, at heart.

Individual organisational rivalry must be forgotten with the objective of meeting all the needs of the patient and family by networking where each group cannot provide all care individually.

Working in partnership

No man is an Island (John Donne)

Each part of the body is required to make a whole functioning being. So if we are busy following our own thing without referring to the rest of the organisations working in palliative care, we will not move on and are bereft in many areas.

Networking for the good of the patient and family is a trade mark of palliative care, especially in resource poor settings where we need to share to give holistic care to our patient. We need to share, respect each other and never put each other down.

We pray that each country will grow in this spirit so that peace and growth can happen when our time comes as well as for those we are caring. We must always remember:

There is an appointed time for everything and a time for every season under Heaven. . .

A time to be born and a time to die.

Ecclesiastes 3.vs1 and 2

Index

Note: *Page numbers in italics refer to illustrations.*

A

Abeokuta, Nigeria 242
Abuja 239–41
Achetti, Father Joseph 141
Addis Ababa 186, 229, 238
Adichie, Chimamanda Ngozi 241
Africa vii, xi–xvi, 19–22, 34–6, 38–41,
    47–50, 52–4, 56–7, 149–50, 152–
    7, 173, 184–6, 189–91, 193–9,
    206–7, 226–8, 238–42
  Anglophone 253–4
  Central 234
  East 53, 243
  Francophone 114, 193, 253–4
  Saharan 132
  South *see* South Africa
  southern 69
  sub-Saharan 64, 275
  West 243, 247, 271
African Organisations for Research and
    Training in Cancer (AORTIC)
    160
African Oxford Cancer Foundation
    (AfrOx) 253
African Palliative Care Association *see*
    APCA
Agaba, Martin xiv, 109–11, *111*, 112,
    180
Agency for Personal Services Overseas
    see APSO
Aid Commission, 193
AIDS Congress, Mexico 213
AIDS Support Organisation (TASO)
    87, 88, 119
Aikenhead, Mother Mary 43
Ainsdale 192–3
Aisha 122–3
Akpan xiv, 60–2, *62*
Alamira, Gudo 96
Alexander, Lynn xiii
Al Faki, Adam 252
Amandua, Jacinto xvi, 88–9, *165*

Amery, Justin 157
Amharic 237
Amin, Idi 64, 106
Amukoko, Lagos 59
Ann Arbor University 238
Antoni 151
Anua, Uyo, Nigeria xiv, 28–9, 62
AORTIC (African Organisations for
    Research and Training in Cancer)
    160
APCA (African Palliative Care
    Association) 76, 132, 150, 159,
    183–4, 195–6, 198–9, 232, 234,
    245, 254, 267
APSO (Agency for Personal Services
    Overseas) 66, 101, 188–9, 200–1,
    261
Arusha, Tanzania 198
ARVs (antiretrovirals) 36–8, 65, 91, 98,
    104, 107, 119, 121, 212, 227,
    254, 269
Aryampa, Rosette *112*
Asians 64, 106
Asiimwe, Beatrice *112*
Asmerom, Dr 235–6
Au, Albert 272–3
Australia xii, 45, 106

B

Babirye, Betty xiii
Bailhache, Anne 93, 193, 204
Baingana, Dr Sheila 98
Bamenda xv, 242–3, 245–6, 254
Banso Baptist Hospital (BBH) 242–3,
    245–6, 253
Bantu 69
Barat, Sophie 260
Barrett, Dr Norman 44
Barugahare, George *112*
Bashir xiv, 76–7, *77*
Bazirake, Stephen 95

BBH (Banso Baptist Hospital) 242–3, 245–6, 253
Belletu 235–6
Benares 30, 211
Benares Hindu University 29
Benedict, Pope 119
Bennett, Jane 167, 193
Bennett, Jim xv–xvi, *167*, 193, *194*, 261
Betty xiv, 80–2, *82*, 104, 106
Biafra xiv, 24, 28, 58, 60, 240
Biafran War 28, 240–1
Bible 54, 70, 121, 136, 142
Bifabusa, Nurse Betty *112*
Bigombe, Betty 63
Birakurtaki, Jerith 106
Bissaso, Alice *168*
Bissaso, Anne (Little Anne) *168*
Bissaso, Mary *168*
Bissaso, Molly *168*
Black Lion Hospital, Ethiopia 237
Blackrock Clinic, Dublin 236
Blair, Cherie xvi, *166*
Blue Book xiv, 91–2, *92*, 114, 159, 242, 253
Boland, Sister Doreen 260
Botswana 195
British Empire 212
British Government 88, 199
British High Commission (BHC) 59, 67, 75, 80, 83, 204, 248
British Library iv
Brittany 193
Broekenhuizen, Ria (formerly Van der Hel) 204–5
Buganda 133, 214
Bujunbura health centre 105
Bukenya, Amina 98, *112*
Bukenya, Hassan *112*
Bunyoro 104
Burkitt, Dennis 81–2
Burkitt's lymphoma xiv, 81, *82*, 122, *157*
Byabazaire, Rt Rev. Dr Deogratias (Catholic Bishop) 105
Byaruhanga, Steven 106, *188*

C

CAFOD (Catholic Association for Overseas Development) 66, 189–90
Cairdas 158
Calcutta 30
Callan, Father Bob 42
Camboni Sisters 141, 253
Cameroon 198, 229, 242–6, 253–4
  Baptist mission 244
Canada xii, 35, 45, 66, 244
Cancer Institute xv, 81, 157
Cancer Pain Relief (WHO, 1986) 86
Canossian Sisters 25, 46, 47
Cape Comerin 30
Cape Town xv, 196, 273
Carl, Brother 106
CAPS, Harare 57
Cara Counselling Center 233
Cassidy, Dr Sheila iv, xv, *218*, 220–1, 268
Catholicism/Catholic Church xii, 25, 55, 79, 119, 121, 129, 131, 135–6, 151, 176, 190, 199, 256, 260
Catholic and Protestant Mission 55
Catholic Archdiocese of Mbarara 100, 205
Catholic Association for Overseas Development (CAFOD) 66, 189–90
Catholic Fund for Overseas Development 189
Catholic Hill of Kampala 55
Catholic Mission Hospital 253
Catholic Mission in Maryland 58
Catholic Sisters 232
CD count 37, 71, 121
CD4 count 37, 99
CEBEMO 199
Celtic spirituality 131
Centre for Palliative Care in Nigeria (CPCN) 229, 242
Centre of Excellence for Clinical Palliative Care, Makindye, Uganda xv, 202, *202*
Centre of Khartoum (RICK) xv, 252
Chad 144, 278

Chan, Sister Lucia *30*
Charlie, Father 94
Charlotte, Specialist Palliative Care
    Nurse xv, *119*
China/Chinese 35, 86, 194, 235, 257
Chinese Communism 235
Christ, Jesus xii, 42, 121, 123, 134, 136,
    144, 210, 261, 278
Christian Medical Commission iv, vi,
    50, 275
Christianity 134, 251
Churchill, Winston 65
Cistercian Sisters 94
Civil Service Third World Fund 53
Civil Society Fund 188
Civil Society of Ireland 190
Clark, Prof. David 203
Clarke, Dr Ian 209–10
*Clinical Guide to HIV/AIDS Palliative
    Care in Africa* 114
Clinton, Bill 82
CME (continuing medical education) 84
Combined Scientific Conference on the
    Management of Advanced Cancer
    63
Comic Relief 190
Commissioner of Health Services 88
Confucianism 131
Congo 227
Congo Brazzaville 253
Connemara 261
Coop, Howard 209
CORDAID 199, 205
Côte d'Ivoire 254
Course in Palliative Clinical Care
    (CPCC) 114, 159, 265
CPCC *see* Course in Palliative Clinical
    Care
CPCN (Centre for Palliative Care in
    Nigeria) 229, 242
Cromwell, Shalunga 233–4
Crucis, Sister 232
Curtain, Philip 72, 79
CV 211, 277
CVWs (Community Volunteer
    Workers)107–9, 114

D

Daughters of Mary and Jesus (DMJ)
    101
Davidson, Alice 64, 191
DELTA (Development Education
    Leadership Team in Action) 255
Department for International
    Development *see* DFID
Department of Cancer and Palliative
    Care 88, 237
Department of Community
    Occupational and Family
    Medicine 46
Department of Medicine 99, 156, 232,
    249
Department of Surgery 72
Development Education Leadership
    Team in Action (DELTA) 255
DFID (Department for International
    Development) 99, 199–200, 250
Diana, Princess of Wales 194–5
Diana, Princess of Wales Memorial
    Fund 90, 189, 193–5, 197–9,
    232, 266
Dillon, Martin 75
Diploma in Palliative Care 229
Director of Business and Support
    Services 265
Director of CEBEMO 199
Director of Medical Services in Uganda
    75
Distance Learning Diploma *see* DLD
Distance Learning Programme 237
District CVWs 109
District Health Headquarters 103
Dix, Olivia 194
DLD (Distance Learning Diploma) 73,
    99, 114, 156, 199, 202–3, 233,
    237, 242
DMJ (Daughters of Mary and Jesus)
    101
Donegal 262
Donohoe, Mary 203
Douala, Cameroon 242, 244
Dowling, Bishop Kevin 138, 176, 261
Drug Authority, Uganda 85
d'Souza, Catherine xv, 246, 251

Dublin iv, 43
Duggan, Dr Mirian 90

E

Eames, Aidan 203
Eastern Europe 45, 260–1
Ebola 99
ECC 144, 278
Ecuador 204
Edge Hill University, Liverpool 107
Eldoret, Kenya 53–4, 67, 80
Elfick, Hilary iv–v, 19–20, 103
Elizabeth II, HM Queen 231
Enniskillen 81
Entebbe 117
Entebbe Road, Kampala 88, 260
Enugu, Nigeria 242
Epstein Barr virus 81
Eritrea 235
Ethiopia xv, 173, 186, 198, 226, 229, 234–8
Ethos and Spirit of Hospices in Africa vi, 149, 264, 278
Europe 42, 260

F

Fabiola xii, xvi, 42, *161*
Falster, Anne *188*
Father Damien Society of Blessed Sacrament Parish, Singapore 66
Fatumnbi, Mrs Sola xv, 59, *239*
Fazal House 53, 73
Fielding, Autumn xiii, xv, *171*
Finch, Lucy xv, 230, *231*
Finch, Tony 230
Fitzgerald, Gretchen 188
Fitzgibbon, Brian xiv, *95*, 98
Fitzgibbon, Clare xiv, *95*, 98–9
Florence 70–1
FMM (Franciscan Missionary of Mary) 55
FOHUI (Friends of Hospice Uganda in Ireland) 201
Foley, Kathy 203
Forestry Commission 230
Fovea Aged Home 43

Frame, Dr Karen xiv, *95*, 99
Frame, Luke 95
France xvi, 43, 167, 191, 193, 253, 260–1
Franciscan Missionary of Mary (FMM) 55
Franciscan Sisters 63, 90
Frangipani xi, xvi, 163
Freetown xv, 248–51
Frehiwot (aka Frey) xv, 235–6, *236*
French xiv, 91–2, 114, 242, 253, 260
Friday Fast scheme 190
Friends of Hospice Uganda in Ireland (FOHUI) 201
Frost, Michael 80, 82–3, 204

G

Gabba 81
Gabriel 247, 250
Gaffer, Dr Nahla xv, 252, *252*
Gahire, Rose 254
Gambia 248
Garnier, Madame Jeanne 43
Gavin, Noel xiii
Geneva iv, vi, xi, 50, 86–8, 237, 275
Geriatric Medicine in Liverpool 29
Ghana 50, 248, 250
Ghandi 28
Global Fund 38, 229–30
Goh, Dr Cynthia xiv, xv, 25, *30*, 48, 155, *218*
Graham, Jane 238
Greenwood, Anthony 225
Gulu 63, 99
Gwyther, Dr Liz 114

H

Hadija 101
HA *see* Hospice Africa
HAI (Hospice Africa Ireland) 43, 201, 203
  Board 201
Haile Mariam 235–6
Haile Selassie, Emperor 234–5
Harare, Zimbabwe 56–7
Hargreaves, Paul 64

Harnett, Dr Ita xiii
Harold's Cross 43
Hassan (driver) 96, 98
HATN (Hospice Africa the
    Netherlands) 100, 205
HAU *see* Hospice Africa Uganda
Health Sector Strategic Plan, five-year
    226
Health Services Coordinator 101, 275
Health Services Manager 123
Health Strategic Plan 88
Heavey, Aidan 108
Henock 236
Hetherington, Nigel 263
Higgins, Dr Stephen 203
Hills, Dr Judith xv, *207*, 208
Hinshaw, Prof. Dan 238
Hoey, Sister Laurence 58–9
Hoima v, xiv, 19, 93–4, 103–7, 109,
    207
Holland 199
Holy Land 42
Hospice Africa (HA) vi, viii, x–xiii, xv,
    21, 25, 46, 51–2, 62, 64, 93, 114–
    15, 149–50, 177, 198–9, 278
    Board of Trustees 79
    and Hospice Africa Uganda 21, 278
Hospice Africa Foundation 79
Hospice Africa Ireland (HAI) 43, 201,
    203
Hospice Africa the Netherlands
    (HATN) 100, 205
Hospice Africa Uganda (HAU) iv–v,
    xi–xiii, 19–21, 53, 63, 66–7, 72–
    3, 88–9, 92, 96, 101, 107, 113–
    17, 141, 155–6, 158–9, 184–5,
    188–9, 197–9, 216, 230, 236,
    259, 277–8
    Annual Report 127
    Board vii
    Boards of Governance 160
    Kampala 98
    Makindye xvi, 168
    Special Children's Programme 157
Hospice Africa UK (HA (UK)) 189,
    191, 193, 243

Hospice Africa USA (HA (USA)) xv,
    207–8
Hospice Africa Worldwide vi, 188
Hospice and Palliative Care Association
    of Nigeria (HPCAN) 241
Hospice Board 224
Hospice Care Association of Singapore
    25, 47
Hospice Ethiopia 237–8
Hospice Nigeria 59
HPCAN (Hospice and Palliative Care
    Association of Nigeria) 241
Human Development Index (HDI) 184,
    227, 247

I

Ibadan, Nigeria 28, 59, 239–40, 242
Ibanda 99–100
Ibibio 60
Ibo 60
IDI (Infectious Disease Institute) 155–6
IHF *see* Irish Hospice Foundation
Iyekat, Hellen 96, 98
Ilorin, Nigeria 242
India 25, 29–30, 45, 95, 144, 211, 241,
    278
Indians 212
Infectious Disease Institute (IDI) 155–6
International Community Health 25
International Development 199
International Director v, xi
International Health 29
International Missionary Training
    Hospital in Drogheda 235
International Orthodox Churches 238
International Programmes 165, 167
International Rotarians 95
International Rotary 96
*International Volunteering in Palliative
    Care* 277
Iomaidh (Omey) Island 261
Ireland iv, xiii, xv, 24–5, 27, 43, 53, 55,
    58, 66, 101, 114, 116, 188–9,
    199–203, 259–62
Irish Aid 188, 200–3, 232
Irish Civil Society Fund 188

Irish Hospice Foundation (IHF) xiii, 66, 203
Irish Kiltegan Father 59
Irish National Teachers Organization 189
Irish Palliative Care Association 203
Irish Sisters of Charity 43
Irish Teachers' Union 66
Ishywishy the First (Hospice Cat) 80, *81*
Island Hospice, Harare, Zimbabwe 54, 56–7, 247
Italy 141
Iyekat, Helen *112*

J

Jack, Barbara 107
Jackson 80, *81*, 96, 98
Jacobson, Mark 198
Jagwe, Dr Jack xvi, 85, 87–9, 198, 225, 229, 232, 237, 242, 247, 252, 254, 266–7, *267*
James xv, xvi, *157*, *164*, 268–9
Jane 101
Japan xv, 218
Jerith, Nurse xv, 107, *183*
Jersey 193, 199, 204
Jersey Overseas Aid Commission 81, 204
John (interpreter) 76
John (patient) 275
John, Dr Laurence 99
John Moore's University 52
Joigny, France 260, 261
Joint Medical Store, Nsambaya 55
Jordan, Father Brendan, MHM 141

K

Kabalagala 74
Kabale 100
Kabale Road 101
Kaganzi, Nurse Beatrice *112*
Kahuma, Innocent *188*
Kakande, Brigid (volunteer nurse) xiv, 76, 77, *77*

Kakande, Prof. Ignatius 72, *75*, 76, 79, 157
Kaleeba, Noerine 64, 65, 207
Kamara, Francis 251
Kampala v, vii, xiii–xvi, 21, 54, 63, 67, 72–3, 80–1, 93–4, 97, 99–101, 103, 105–6, 115–16, 186
Kasigwa, Betty 104, *105*, 106, *188*
Kasili, Prof. E. 49, 224
Katabalwa, Isaac *188*
Katabira, Dr Elly 158
Kateregga, Henry Mary 72–3, 79–80, 199, 214
Kateregga House 80, 202, 204
Kayanja, Prof. Federic I.B. 95
Kazibwe, Margaret *168*
Kazooba, Charles Tushabomwe 96
Kebirungi, Harriet 98
Kelly, Joan (Joan Scheer) 100, 205, *205*
Kemp, Margaret 235
Kennelly, Dr Siobhan xvi, 203, *265*
Kenya 53–4, 79, 84, 87, 105, 195, 224, 229, 275
    Ministry of Health 224
Kenya Airways 271
Kerala 30
Kevin, Mother 55
Kevina 71
Khartoum xv, 251–2
Kibirege, Jane *75*
Kikule, Dr Ekie 149
Kileleshwa, Nairobi, Kenya 54
Kiltegan Fathers 58
Kirambi Community Health & Development Programme 255
Kisembo, John *188*
Kitovu 74
Kitovu Home Care 34
Kitovu Mission Hospital, Masaka 64, 74, 207
Kitovu Mobile, Masaka 90
Kivumbi, James *188*
Kiwanuka, Rose v, xv, 67, 69, 74, *75*, 80, *81*, 86, 116, 155, *197*
Knowsley 29
Kobweme, John *112*
KPMG Ireland 202

Kumbo, Bamenda Province 242
Kyomuhendo, Irene *188*
Kyomuhendo, Robert 106, *188*

L

Lacor Hospital, Gulu 63
Lady's Hospice, Lusaka 232
Lagos, Nigeria 54, 58–9, 62, 239–40,
    242
Lake Albert 108
Lake Victoria, Kampala, Uganda xiv,
    21, 73, 259
Lancaster University 203, 225
Latin Mass 129
Lee Kuan Yew 86
Leng, Dr Mhoira xv, *158*
LHH (Little Hospice Hoima) 94, 103,
    105–10, 113, 265
Liberia 247
Lighthouse, Lilongwe, Malawi 229
Lilongwe 229
Lilongwe Catholic Diocese HBC
    Programme 230
Linnell, Pat 64
Lions International Club 96
Little Hospice Hoima *see* LHH
Little Red Book of Chairman Mao 235
Liverpool vii, xii, xv, 24, 29, 51–2, 64,
    87, 172, 189, 191–3, 200, 235–6,
    259
Liverpool School of Tropical Medicine
    25, 30, 62, 211, 235
Lloyd-Williams, Anne 194–5, *196*, 232
Lord's Resistance Army 63–4
Lucy (secretary) *105*
Lugazi, Uganda 76
Luke (driver) 74–6, *81*
Lule, Dr Gerald *112*
Lusaka 232
Lusophone Africa 253
Lutheran World 75
Luxembourg 262
Lynch, Dr Maura xvi, *265*
Lyon 43, 253

M

McAleese, President Mary xv–xvi, *117*,
    165
McAleese, Martin *165*
McAleish, Joan 82–3
McElvaine, Dave 57
McGannon, Michelle 99
McGoldrick, Jane 201
McGoldrick, Micheal xv, *75*, 200–1,
    201
McTiernan, Father Jim 94
Makerere 85, 93, 116, 241
Makerere Medical School 80, 95
Makerere University, Uganda xiv, 72,
    81, 87, 92, 156–7, 159, 195
    Palliative Care Unit 157–8
Makindye xiv–xvi, 53, 73–5, 93, 108–9,
    113, 115, 165, 167, 195, 202
Makumbi, James 56, 63, 85
Malawi 89, 182, 198, 226–7, 229–30,
    232
Malaysia 25, 30
Mandela, Nelson 127
Maniraguha, Bernard 96
Margaret (patient) xiv, *70*, 70–1
Marge (charity shop helper) xv, *192*
Martin, Mother Mary xv, 28, *172*
Mary (patient) 118–21
Mary McAleese Lecture Theatre 116,
    202
Masaka, Uganda 68, 73, 79, 101, 207
Masters Programme in International
    Community Health 235
Mayanja, Harriet 158
Mbara University Teaching Hospital
    (MUTH) 94
Mbaraka, Fazal xiv, *53*, 53–6, 58–9,
    62–3, 66–7, 73, 76, 80
Mbarara xv, 78, 93–6, 98–101, 115,
    186, 205, 215, 260–1
    Lord Mayor xiv, 97
    Regional Hospital 101
    University of Science and
        Technology 87, 93–4
Mbabazi, Irene *188*
Medical Missionary of Mary *see*
    MMMs

Meeting Point 104
Merriman, Bernard xiv, 26
Merriman, Dr Anne (*photos*) *ii, viii, 24,*
    30, 70, 74, 81, 117, 166–8, 197,
    233, 239
Merriman, Hannah xiii, xv, *175, 188*
Merriman, Father Joseph, SDB 259
Merriman, Josephine (Josie) (Anne's
    mother) 24–26, *26,* 27, 29
Merriman, Thomas Joseph (Toddy)
    (Anne's father) 24–26, *26*
Merriman House xiv, 74, 201, 204
MHM (Mobile Hospice Mbarara) v,
    xiv–xvi, 66, 93–5, 96–102, 113,
    164, 179, 186, 190, 206, 265
Mijumbi, Lucy 106
Mikajo, Peter xv, *223*
Mildmay Centre for Palliative Care of
    HIV/AIDS 91, 183, 184, 199–
    200, 229
Mildmay International 107
MMMs (Medical Missionary of Mary)
    xv, 24–5, 27–9, 58–9, 90, 172,
    176, 189
    Foundations 235
Mobile Hospice Mbarara *see* MHM
Moi University 54, 229
Moloney, Phil 101, 261–2
Mombasa, Kenya 275
Montfort Fathers 94
Moody, Raymond A. 136
Moore, Jane 48
Moran, Mary 94
Mount, Dr Balfour 35
Mpanga Sebuyira, Dr Lydia xv, 155–6,
    156, 196
Mucunguzi, Jackson *112*
Mugneyi, Peter 269
Mugume, Edwin 96
Muhammad 134
Mukankuranga, Grace 254
Mukasa, Mary *75*
Mukwananzi, Sambhulo (Sam) 247
Mulago, Uganda 76, 122, 155, 158
Mulago Hospital xv, 85, 87, 158
Mulanje, Malawi 232
Muliyil, Dr J.P. 144, 278

Munda, Charles 248–51
Munyonyo, Kampala, Uganda xvi, 21,
    165, 167–8, 273
Murphy, Margaret 94
Murphy, Oliver 94
Murray, Eugene xiii, 203
Murrell, Lynn 208
Museveni, President Yoweri Kaguta 64,
    82, 88, 98, 191, 200, 210
Musitwa, Godfrey *112*
Muslims 54, 67, 121, 123, 129, 131,
    134, 139, 251
Mustafa (patient) 121
MUTH (Mbara University Teaching
    Hospital) 94
Muvaney, Clare xiii, xvi, 162
Muyenga, Uganda 73–4, 78, 199
Mwazi (nurse trainer) 253
Mwebesa, Eddie 246
Myton Hamlet Hospice, Warwick 51

N

Nairobi xii, 21–2, 46, 48–50, 54, 67, 79,
    145, 224, 267, 275
Nairobi Hospice xii, xiv, 48–50, 53–4,
    224, 229, 232, 254, 275
    Board 54, 224
    Charitable Trust 48
    first Medical Director 48, 224
Nairobi Hospital 49, 224
Nakurru, Kenya 275
Namugongo, Uganda 80
Namugongo Camboni Convent and
    Retreat Centre 259
Namukwaya, Dr Liz xv, *138,* 158
Nasasira, Naomi *75,* 79
Natete, Kampala, Uganda 80
National Drug Authority, Uganda 87,
    241, 266
National Health Plan, Uganda 85
National Health Service (NHS, UK) 46
National Strategic Framework, Uganda
    226
National Teaching Hospital, Zambia
    233, 266

National University Hospital, Singapore
224
National University, Singapore 25, 30,
46, 106
Nawangi, Catherine xv, 183, 238, *238,*
243–5, *246*, 252–3
Naziwa Octivia, PC Nurse xv, *138*, *147*
Ndamira, Andrew 98
Ndebba xiv, 73, 75, 80–2, 199
Ndenikum, George 242, 245–6, *246*
Ndi Moyo hospice, Salima, Malawi 230
Needham, Sister Rosemary 55
Nesige, Deo *188*
Netherlands 204–5
NHS (UK) *see* National Health Service
Nigeria xii, xv–xvi, 22, 25, 28–9, 49–
50, 54, 56, 58–61, 67, 87, 104,
130, 226, 229, 239–43
Ministry of Health 59, 229
Nile Special xiv, 105–6
Northern Hospital, Liverpool 51
Norway 107
Nouwen, Henri 259
Nsambya, Uganda 55, 69, 72, 204
Nsambya Mission Hospital, Uganda 67,
69, 73, 80, 90, 200
Home Care 34, 90
Nsambya VMM House xiv, 67–8, *68*
Nsimenta, Rosemary *188*
Nyeri, Kenya 275

O

Obote, President Milton 64
Observatory in End of Life Care
(OELC) 203, 225
Obudu, Nigeria 28
O'Connor, John 201
O'Connor, Margaret 201
OELC (Observatory in End of Life
Care) 203, 225
Old Swan, Liverpool 191–3
Olkon, Dr Pius 67
Omey (Iomaidh) Island 261
Onitsha, Nigeria 59
Opito, Dr Steven 72
Overseas Aid Commission, Jersey 204

Overseas Development Administration
(UK) 199
O'Donohue, John 51, 66, 93, 131–2,
169, 262
O'Neill, Joe 206
Owollu, Catherine 67
Owokunda, Deborah *112*
Oxford Brookes University 229

P

Pahl, Nick 247, 249
Pakistan 53
Palliative Care Association (PCA)
African *see* APCA
Cameroon 246
France 243
Malawi (PCAM) 232
Rwanda (PCAR) 254
Sierra Leone 248
Uganda *see* PCAU
Palliative Care Unit, Makerere
University 157–8
Palmer, Derek 107
Papos xiii
Pathak, Professor Pat 95–6, 98
Patrick (driver) 59–60
Paul, Archbishop xv, 205, *206*
PCA *see* Palliative Care Association
PCAM (Palliative Care Association of
Malawi) 232
PCAR (Palliative Care Association of
Rwanda) 254
PCAU (Palliative Care Association of
Uganda) xv, 76, 101, 109, 141,
156, 184, 195, 197–8
Peace Corps 187
Peck, Scott 128, 188, 259, 264
Penang, Malysia 25
People Living With AIDS (PLWA)
103, 107
PEPFAR (President's Emergency Plan
for AIDS Relief) 38, 191, 206,
208
Petefield & Bodgener 72
Peter (patient) 122

Phipps, Dr David xvi, 51, 52, 64, *167*, 231
Phipps, Lesley vii, xvi, 51–2, 64, *167*, 189–90, 192, 264, 268–9
Pierce, Pauline 201
PLWA (People Living With AIDS) 103, 107
Poland 233
Polish Hospice 233
Polish Palliative Care 233
Polish Sisters 232
Poor Clares 94
Port Harcourt 28, 62
Powell, Faith Mwangi 195
Presbyterian Mission Hospital, Mulanje, Malawi 232
President's Emergency Plan for AIDS Relief *see* PEPFAR
Prins Fund 205
Probasco, Abby xiii, xv, xvi, 157, 165, 166
Provincial Hospital, Bamenda Town, Cameroon 246
Purcell, Anne xv, 191, *192*
Purcell, Pete xv, 191, *192*

Q

QEUCH (Queen Elizabeth University College Hospital, Blantyre, Malawi) 231–2
Quinn, Brid 101
Quinn, Emily xiii

R

Rabwoni, Martha v, xvi, *75*, 96, 98, 101, *112*, 116, *164*
Radiation and Isotope Centre, Khartoum (RICK) xv, 252
Reach Out Mbuya 141
Redmond, Mary 203
RICK (Radiation and Isotope Centre of Khartoum) xv, 252
Robert (driver) *105*
Robert (patient) xiv, 81–3
Rose Project 203
Rotarians 75, 95–8, 106

Rotary International 96
Royal College of Physicians, London 45
Royal Marsden Cancer Hospital, London 46
Ruwambaya, Catherine 183
Russell, Dr James xv, *248*, 248–50
Russia 235
Rutembegwa House, Uganda 202
Rwanda xvi, 227, 243, 254–5
    Ministry of Health 254

S

Sacred Heart Hospital, Obudu, Nigeria xiv, 24
Sacred Heart Missionary Fathers 73
Sacred Heart Sisters 260
Sago Lane, Singapore 35, 86
St Anne's Hospital, Zimbabwe 56
St Christopher's Hospice, London 43, 45, 59, 151, 256
St Clare 94
St Francis 94
St Francis Xavier 258
St Helen's, Merseyside 29
St Joseph's Hospice xiv, 30, 43, 45, 151
St Joseph's Home for the Aged, Singapore 46, 86
St Luke's Hospital, Anua, Uyo, Nigeria xiv, 28, 44, 59, 60, 62
St Mark's Gospel 217
St Mary's Hospice, Birmingham 51, 53
St Theresa's gynaecological ward, Nsambya Hospital, Uganda 69
St Vincent's Hospital, Dublin 43
Salesians 26, 195, 259
Sali, John 72
Salima, Malawi 230
Salima Catholic Parish HBC Initiative 230
Sarah (carer) xv, 120, 138
Saunders, Dame Cicely vii, *vii*, xii, xiv, 29, 34, 43–4, *44*, 45, 50, 151, 154, 155, 256, 259, 269, 273
Savedy church 217
Scandinavia 56
Scheer, Joan *see* Kelly, Joan

Scheer, Ronald xv, 100, 205, *205*
SCIAF (Scottish Catholic International
Aid Fund) 66, 82–3, 87, 189
Scotland 66, 158, 261
Scottish Catholic International Aid
Fund *see* SCIAF
Sebusubi, Fred 91
Second World War 260
Senegal 50, 248
Sepulveda, Cecilia 88, 237
Shanahan, Bishop (Nigeria) 257
Shaw, Dr Rosalie 25, 48
Shepherd's Hospice, Sierra Leone 247–
50
Shoa 234
Sierra Leone 226, 227, 240, 247–51
Simensen, Bjorn 107
Simmons, Carla 90
Singapore xii–xiii, xv, 21–2, 25, 30–1,
35, 46–8, 54, 66, 84, 86–7, 106,
155, 200, 218, 224
Ministry of Health 86
Singapore Community Chest 47
Sirengo, Nurse Brigid xiv, 48, *48*
Soba University Teaching Hospital 252
Soins Palliatifs (HA France) 167, 193,
253
South Africa 24, 39, 45, 138, 191, 196,
223, 249, 254, 261
South America xii, 45
South East Asia 45
Sponsheimer, Michaela *112*
Soyannwo, Olaiten xv, 229, *239*
Ssengooba, Dr Jenny *115*
Ssentoogo, Henry *75*, 79
Stack, Triona *202*
Stephen (general assistant) *105*
Stephen (patient) 249–50
Stephenson, Celia 55, 64
Stjernsward, Jan v, xi, *xi*, xii, xiv, 87, 105
Strada, Maria della 42
Stu (volunteer) xvi, *166*
Sudan 227, 251
Southern 253
Sunanda Ray 65
Survive 75
Swahili 243

Sweden xii

T

Takeda, Dr Fumikazu xv, *218*
Tambo, Lamek 229
Tan, Sister Geraldine xiv, 25, *30*, 46–7,
47, 48
Tan, Sister Mary 46
Tank Hill 73
Tanzania 50, 76, 80, 89, 198, 226
Tasma, David 43, 151
TASO (The AIDS Support
Organisation) 34, 64–5, 87, 90,
119, 158, 207
Teddy (patient) 66
THET (Tropical Health Education
Trust) 99
Tibayungwa, John *112*
Tibumanye, Dr Stella xiv, 103–5, *105*,
106
Tih, Prof. 242–3
Tiyanjane Clinic, Queen Elizabeth
University College Hospital,
Blantyre, Malawi 232
Tomas (volunteer) xvi, *166*
Trinity College Dublin 81
Tropical Health Education Trust
(THET) 99
Tsigereda, Sister xv, 237–8, *238*
Tugumisirize, Scholar *112*
Tullow Oil of Ireland 108
Tumwine, Wilson xiv, 95, *97*
Tutu, Desmond 24
Twinomugoni, Nurse Honest *112*
Twycross, Dr Robert xv, *160*

U

Ubuntu xci, 127, 131–3
UCH *see* University College Hospital
Uganda vi–vii, 19, 54–6, 62–7, 84–5,
87–91, 105–7, 113–17, 133, 141,
182–6, 189–91, 196–9, 209–10,
213–17, 226–7, 261–3, 268–70,
277–9
Government 200
Ministry of Finance 209

Ministry of Foreign Affairs 188
Ministry of Health 56, 63, 67, 85–9,
    91, 104, 108, 159, 165, 185, 216,
    229, 237, 255, 266
    Northern 109
Uganda Peoples Defence Force (UPDF)
    73
Ugandans 65, 67, 68, 73, 76, 78–9, 85,
    108, 117–18, 120, 127, 152, 183,
    185–6, 201, 213–14, 263, 264
Umodzi (children's programme,
    Malawi) 231
United Kingdom iv, vii, xi, xv, 28, 48,
    51, 56, 60, 63–4, 66, 88–9, 98–9,
    188–91, 193–4, 230–1, 247, 275
United States 8 45, 76, 82, 116, 190,
    198, 206, 245, 249, 265
United States Agency for International
    Development (USAID) 208, 232,
    238
Universiti Sains Malaysia (USM) 25, 30
University College Dublin 28
University College Hospital, Blantyre
    232
University College Hospital, Ibadan xv,
    28, 60, 229, 239–41
University Medical School, Freetown,
    Sierra Leone 249
University of Aberdeen 158
University of Cameroon 254
University of Freetown 251
University of Ibadan 59, 240
University of Wisconsin 267
UPDF (Uganda Peoples Defence Force)
    73
Urua Akpan, Nigeria 59
USAID (United States Agency for
    International Development) 208,
    232, 238
USM (Universiti Sains Malaysia) 25, 30
Uyo, Nigeria xiv, 59–60, 62

V

Van der Hel, Prins 204–5
Van der Hel, Ria (now Ria
    Broekenhuizen) 204–5
Vanier, Jeanne 259

Vatican II 129
Veronica 104
Victo, Dr Ndiforchu *246*
Victoria (Lake), Kampala, Uganda 106
Viegas, Osborn 106
Vietnam 244
Virgin Mary 119
VMM (Volunteer Missionary
    Movement) 55, 67
Voices for Hospice, London 103
Volunteer Missionary Movement
    (VMM) 55, 67
VSO (Voluntary Service Overseas) 98–
    9, 200, 245–6

W

Waligo, John Mary 132
Walker, Esther xv, *248*, 248–52
Walton Hospital, Liverpool 87
Ward, Ann 60
Wefuan, Dr Jonah 245–6, *246*
West Indies 29
Whiston Hospital, Liverpool 29
White Fathers 94, 106
Williamson, Jimmy 51
Wisconsin 249, 267
Wishy Washy 80
Wooldridge, Mike 48
Wooldridge, Ruth 48, 254
World Council of Churches 50, 144
World Heath Organisation 34, 86

Y

Yaoundé, Cameroon 242–3, 254

Z

Zambia xv, 198, 226, 229–30, 232–4,
    236
Zaramba, Sam 75
Zaria, Nigeria 242
Zimbabwe xii, 39, 45, 54, 56–7, 223,
    247
Zirimenya, Dr Ludovik xvi, *166*